easy piano classics

Selected and Edited

by James Bastien

The Bastien Older Beginner Piano Library

Published by Kjos West.
4382 Jutland Dr., San Diego, CA 92117

ISBN 0-8497-5042-3

Preface

EASY PIANO CLASSICS is designed to supplement **THE OLDER BEGINNER PIANO COURSE, LEVEL 2.** However, this volume may be used for study and enjoyment with another piano course, or as an independent literature book. This volume contains representative four-period literature appropriate for collegiate study (secondary piano students) or for private study.

The selections in the first part of the book (Baroque through Contemporary periods) are in original form and are set in approximate order of difficulty within each period. The arranged selections in the last part of the book provide a wide spectrum of famous music from various mediums.

Constant exposure to the literature of the four great eras of music represented in **EASY PIANO CLASSICS** will enable the student to acquire the necessary feeling for imaginative interpretations of the various musical styles that span nearly three centuries. The timeless appeal of this music will provide hours of enjoyment for the pianist and listener.

Suggested Use of Materials with **THE OLDER BEGINNER PIANO COURSE, LEVEL 2**

When the student reaches **page 5,** he is ready to begin . . . .**Musicianship, Level 2** (WP35)

When the student reaches **page 21,** he is ready to begin . . . . **Favorite Melodies the World Over, Level 2** (WP38)

When the student reaches **page 33,** he is ready to begin . . . .**Easy Piano Classics** (WP42)

When the student reaches **page 37,** he is ready to begin . .**Pop, Rock 'N Blues, Book 2** (GP38)

When the student reaches **page 45,** he is ready to begin . . . . . .**Scott Joplin Favorites** (GP90)

CONTENTS
Title Index

CONTENTS
Composer Index

THE BAROQUE PERIOD
(1600-1750)

"The Investiture of Bishop Harold" by Giovanni Battista Tiepolo (1750-1753),
Kaisersaal, Residenz, Würzburg, Germany. Courtesy of Editorial Photocolor Archives, Inc.

The art and architecture of the Baroque period reflect an often bizarre style characterized by ornamental decorations. Especially notable in churches, palaces, and other buildings of the period is the profusion of worldly splendor evident in grandiose designs and elaborate decorations.

The music of the period reflects the decorative art in the use of ornamentation to embellish melodies. Thick and complex polyphonic texture prevails in many composers' works. A sense of drama and urgency is infused in vocal forms such as the cantata, mass, opera, oratorio, and passion, and in instrumental forms such as the concerto, concerto grosso, prelude, fugue, toccata, sonata, and suite. Vibrant rhythms and expressive dissonances heighten tension in many Baroque works.

Much of the Baroque keyboard music written for the harpsichord and clavichord was written in suites comprising separate dance pieces, changing in tempo and meter, but maintaining key unity throughout. The suite (Italian: **Partita, Sonata da Camera;** German: **Suite, Partita, Overture;** French: **Order, Suite;** English: **Lessons**) consists of dances such as the allemande, courante, sarabande, gigue, and others such as the gavotte, musette, bourreé, minuet, and pavane. Each dance piece (movement) is usually written in two sections, called **binary** form, and is generally performed with each section repeated. Other forms of keyboard music from the Baroque period are theme and variation, passacaglia, chaconne, invention, prelude, fugue, choral prelude, ricercare, fantasy, toccata, and concerto.

The two best known Baroque composers are Johann Sebastian Bach and George Frederick Handel, both Germans. Other German Baroque composers include Heinrich Schütz, Samuel Scheidt, Johann Froberger, Dietrich Buxtehude, Johann Pachelbel, Johann Kuhnau, and Georg Telemann. English Baroque composers include William Byrd, John Bull, and Henry Purcell. Notable Italian Baroque composers include Claudio Monteverdi, Arcangelo Corelli, Antonio Vivaldi, and Alessandro and Domenico Scarlatti. Prominent French Baroque composers include Jean Baptise Lully, Francois Couperin, and Jean Philippe Rameau.

THE CLASSICAL PERIOD
(1750-1820)

"Death of Socrates" by Jacques Louis David (1750-1820), oil on canvas, Courtesy of Metropolitan Museum of Art, Wolfe Fund, 1931.

A transitional era of about thirty years, termed "Rococo," between the Baroque and Classical periods set the stage for the emergence of the Classical style. The Rococo musical style was characterized by delicate, frivolous expression designed more to please than to excite the listener. Some of the transitional composers are Francois Couperin, Domenico Scarlatti, and the sons of J. S. Bach.

Emerging from the Baroque period was a new style, highly refined, simple in melodic line and harmonic texture, and unified by symmetrical form. Developing during the early Classical period were expanded instrumental forms such as the sonata allegro and the rondo. The binary dance movements of the Baroque gave way to the **ternary** first movements of most Classical period works (sonata, concerto, chamber music, symphony) which comprised three parts: **exposition** (A), **development** (B), and **recapitulation** (A). Frequently, well-defined melodies were harmonized with triadic harmony, especially in keyboard works with a broken-chord figure called the **Alberti bass** (named after Domenico Alberti who was one of the first to use this type of accompaniment).

Major Classical period composers are Franz Joseph Haydn, Wolfgang Amadeus Mozart, and Ludwig van Beethoven. Others include Domenico Cimarosa and Luigi Cherubini (Italians, best known for their operas), Karl Ditters von Dittersdorf (Viennese, a composer of symphonies, choral music, and operas), Christoph Gluck (Viennese, best remembered for his operas), and Muzio Clementi (Italian, best known today for his keyboard sonatinas).

THE ROMANTIC PERIOD
(1820-1900)

"Stoke-by-Nayland" by John Constable (1836), oil on canvas, 49 ″ x 66½ ″. Courtesy of The Art Institute of Chicago.

The impact of the French Revolution (1789-1794) set the stage for free thinkers and encouraged men of action to independent endeavors. The Romantic period was ushered in by artists who expressed themselves freely and personally. The desire to release emotion and achieve freedom is succinctly expressed in the watchword term "Strum und Drang" ("storm and stress") which comes from a play (1776) by the German author Friedrich von Klinger. Literary works such as Goethe's **Faust** (1808) about a man who defies convention, and novels by E. T. A. Hoffmann (1776-1822) and others inspired musicians to new emotional heights.

Romantic music developed over a period of almost a hundred years. During this time new forms emerged: the art song **(lied)** which combined Romantic poetry with voice and piano; stylized piano music such as the waltz, mazurka, polonaise, and étude (study piece); piano music in free form such as the fantasy, arabesque, rhapsody, romanza, ballade, and nocturne; and symphonic works such as the tone poem (descriptive piece). Programmatic content was expressed in tone poems (by Liszt and others), in symphonic works such as Berlioz' **Symphony Fantastique,** and in piano music such as Mussorgsky's **Pictures at an Exhibition** (later orchestrated in 1923 by Maurice Ravel). Nationalism is prevalent in works such as Chopin's polonaises and mazurkas, Liszt's **Hungarian Rhapsodies,** Smetana's **The Bartered Bride** (opera using patriotic themes) and **The Moldau** (symphonic poem), Borodin's opera **Prince Igor,** and Rimsky-Korsakov's orchestrally resplendent **Scheherezade.**

The music of the Romantic period often contained warm, personal melodies (so tuneful that many have been made into popular songs); expressive indications (**espressivo**—expressively, **dolce**—sweetly, **con amore**—with love, **con fuoco**—with fire; etc.); implied interpretative freedom (**rubato**—rhythmic "give-and-take"); and harmonic color (new chords: altered, seventh, and ninth, and chromatic harmony). Color was intensified in music by the improvements on the piano (enlargement of the piano and perfection of the pedals) and in the orchestra (development of instruments, improvement in technique by the players, and larger scoring by the composers). Virtuoso performers carried playing to new heights (Niccolo Paganini—violinist, 1782-1842; Franz Liszt—pianist, 1811-1886; others). During the Romantic period exaggerated emotional emphasis was displayed in the contradictory qualities of virtuosity (large scale solo pieces, concertos, etc.) and intimacy (salon music such as the subjective piano piece and solo song).

Ludwig van Beethoven (1770-1827) bridged the Classical and Romantic periods in both his life and works, reflecting Classical influences in his early music and Romantic influences in his middle and later years. Significant Romantic period composers are Franz Schubert, Hector Berlioz, Felix Mendelssohn, Frédéric Chopin, Robert Schumann, Franz Liszt, Richard Wagner, Giuseppe Verdi, César Franck, Johannes Brahms, Modest Mussorgsky, Peter Ilyich Tchaikovsky, Anton Dvořák, Edvard Grieg, Nikolai Rimsky-Korsakov, and Giacomo Puccini.

THE CONTEMPORARY PERIOD
(1900-present)

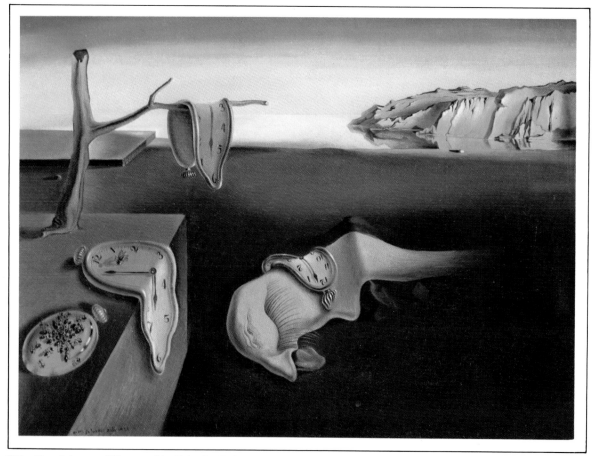

"The Persistence of Memory" by Salvador Dali (1931), oil on canvas 9½ ″ x 13 ″. Collection, The Museum of Modern Art, New York. Given anonymously.

The bridge to the Contemporary period was formed during the last quarter of the nineteenth century through a new painting movement called Impressionism. About 1870 a group of French painters including Claude Monet, Pierre Renoir, Edgar Degas, and others rejected the accepted Romanticism in favor of a new painting style which sought to portray art as the artist's impression of a subject.

Composers Claude Debussy (1862-1918) and Maurice Ravel (1875-1937) portrayed musically these innovations in art and new directions in poetry (Arthur Rimbaud, Paul Verlaine, Stéphane Mallarmé, and others). New sonorities in orchestration and piano music developed which often incorporated extramusical material from art and literature, sometimes contained non-Western melodies and rhythms, introduced new scales (whole-tone, modes) and chord uses (altered chords, parallel motion chords, ninth and eleventh chords), and frequently used unresolved dissonances to portray veiled, illusionary effects.

Twentieth century music reflects the influences of art and literature in a mechanistic, atomic age. The emergence of pleasant sounding, pastel-colored Impressionistic music led to experimentation with twelve-tone music (Arnold Schoenberg—1874-1951, others) which produced cerebral, atonal, often angular and disjunct musical effects. Other twentieth century musical experimentations with electronic music and music for "prepared piano" (use of objects in the piano to produce unusual sounds) have produced totally new mediums for musical expression. Influences such as electronically amplified instruments and jazz, rock, and popular elements are also associated with the period.

Within the "modern" era great style variations are found, ranging from Post-Romanticism (Gustav Mahler—1824-1911, Alexander Scriabin—1872-1915, Sergei Rachmaninoff—1873-1943, others), to Impressionism, to new concepts of melody-tonality-rhythm expressed in the music of composers such as Béla Bartók (1881-1945), Igor Stravinsky (1882-1971), Serge Prokofiev (1891-1952), Aaron Copland (1900-   ), Dmitri Shostakovich (1906-1975), Samuel Barber (1900-1981), Pierre Boulez (1925-   ), and Krzystof Penderecki (1933-   ).

easy piano classics

Selected and Edited
by James Bastien

THE BAROQUE
(1600-1750)

The Early Keyboards

The principle of the vibrating strings used on various instruments (harp, lute, fiddle, keyboard) was an ancient discovery, possibly dating back to prehistoric times when man might have stretched a sinew between two fixed points and made varying pitches by plucking it. Early man might have noticed that thick strings produced lower and fuller tones than thin strings. The basis for varying pitches used in keyboard instruments is found in the stringing of the harp, dating back to the year 3000 B.C. Later man was able to apply a keyboard to the harp string principle to produce tones basically through two means: plucked strings and struck strings.

Precursors of the modern piano are the *eschiquier* (one of the earliest plucked keyboard instruments and possibly ancestor to the harpsichord, in use during the fourteenth century) and the *clavichord* (dating back to the sixth century B.C. when Pythagoras used a *monochord*, an ancestor to the struck stringed clavichord, to experiment with mathematical relationships of musical sounds).

Information about the earliest stringed keyboard instrument is obscure, but historical information about the clavichord reveals that by about the eleventh century a keyboard was applied to a stringed instrument, and by the mid-fifteenth century the clavichord had about twenty to twenty-two strings. By the seventeenth century the clavichord was somewhat standardized in dimensions three to four feet long and two feet wide; some had seventy-seven keys and a pair of strings for each key. The clavichord mechanism produced a tone by means of a small metal tangent attached to the end of the key which struck the strings from below. The tone was delicate and the instrument was used mostly in intimate settings.

The harpsichord became the "concert grand" of the eighteenth century. The tone of this plucked keyboard instrument was fuller and had more carrying power than that of the clavichord. An early version of

German fretted clavichord, first half of the eighteenth century.
The Metropolitan Museum of Art, The Crosby Brown Collection of Musical Instruments, 1889.

German unfretted clavichord, by John Christopher Jesse of Halberstadt, 1765.
The Metropolitan Museum of Art, The Crosby Brown Collection of Musical Instruments, 1889.

the harpsichord was constructed in 1503 by Giovanni Spinetti of Venice. It was oblong and had four octaves. Named after its inventor, the *spinet* (called the *virginal* in England) produced a modest tone by plucking the string with a quill. The German word *flügel*, meaning wing, was adopted to designate the "harpsichord." (In France the harpsichord was called the *clavecin*, and in Italy, *cembalo* or *clavicembalo*.) The wingform shape (identical with the shape of the grand piano) was used by Geronimo of Bologna in 1521. This was the shape preferred by later harpsichord makers who added longer strings and various stops and pedals. By the mid-seventeenth century harpsichords had two keyboards, with two or three strings for each pitch to produce a fuller tone.

Baroque composers adopted their compositions to the capabilities of the clavichord and harpsichord. Since the harpsichord was unable to produce gradual tone gradations (crescendos and decrescendos), composers wrote "echo" effects (a phrase played loud on one keyboard and repeated softly on a second keyboard). The juxtaposition of loud and soft dynamics is called *terrace dynamics*. Because of the lack of sustaining power, especially of the harpsichord, numerous embellishments were added to "fill-in" the sound. Through the use of various stops and cuppling or dampening of the strings, a variety of effects could be made. Composers wrote for the instrument in various styles: Domenico Scarlatti wrote dazzling virtuoso works; Couperin wrote short, delicate, graceful tone pictures; Handel wrote tuneful dances; Rameau wrote a variety of imitative works such as *La Poule (The Hen)* imitating the clucking of a hen; and J. S. Bach wrote substantial preludes, fugues, suites, and even concertos for harpsichord and orchestra. With the invention of the piano in the early 1700's the harpsichord gradually lost favor with musicians, and the piano reigned king until the twentieth century when the beauties of the harpsichord have been rediscovered, and once again the masterpieces of Scarlatti, Couperin, Rameau, and Bach are heard in authentic versions.

Venetian spinettino, 1540.
The Metropolitan Museum of Art, Joseph Pulitzer Bequest, 1953.

Italian harpsichord of the seventeenth century, supported by Tritons, with gilded gesso relief showing the procession of Galatea.
The Metropolitan Museum of Art, The Crosby Brown Collection of Musical Instruments, 1889.

Italian harpsichord by Vincenzo Sodi, three manuals, no stops, Florence, 1779.
The Metropolitan Museum of Art, The Crosby Brown Collection of Musical Instruments, 1889.

Henry Purcell (1659-1695) was the greatest English composer of the Baroque era. He held various posts as singer, organist and composer. He wrote an opera *Dido and Aeneas*, music for plays, songs, instrumental music, and some harpsichord music. His music reflects vocal qualities of lyricism and great expressiveness.

Air

Henry Purcell

Georg Philipp Telemann (1681-1767) was a German church musician and composer. He was the musical director of five churches in Hamburg. He wrote a prodigious amount of music which included passions, operas, overtures, and keyboard works. He was a friend of Bach and Handel. Handel once remarked that Telemann, who was a prolific composer, could write a vocal motet in eight parts as easily as anyone could write a letter!

Gavotte

Georg Philipp Telemann

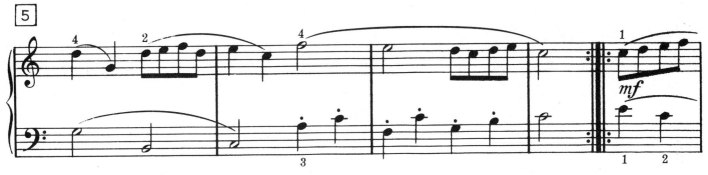

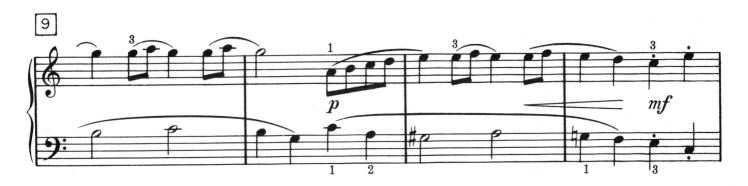

WP42

14 **Francois Couperin (1668-1733)** was an organist, harpsichordist, theorist, teacher and composer. This great French musician was surnamed "Le Grand" because of his superiority as an organist. He wrote organ music, chamber music, vocal music, and music for the harpsichord. This piece is from *Pieces de Clavecin.*

Le Petit Rien*

(from "Pieces de Clavecin")

Francois Couperin

Le Petit Rien means "a little trifle." This title is similar to *Bagatelle* which also means "a trifle."

15

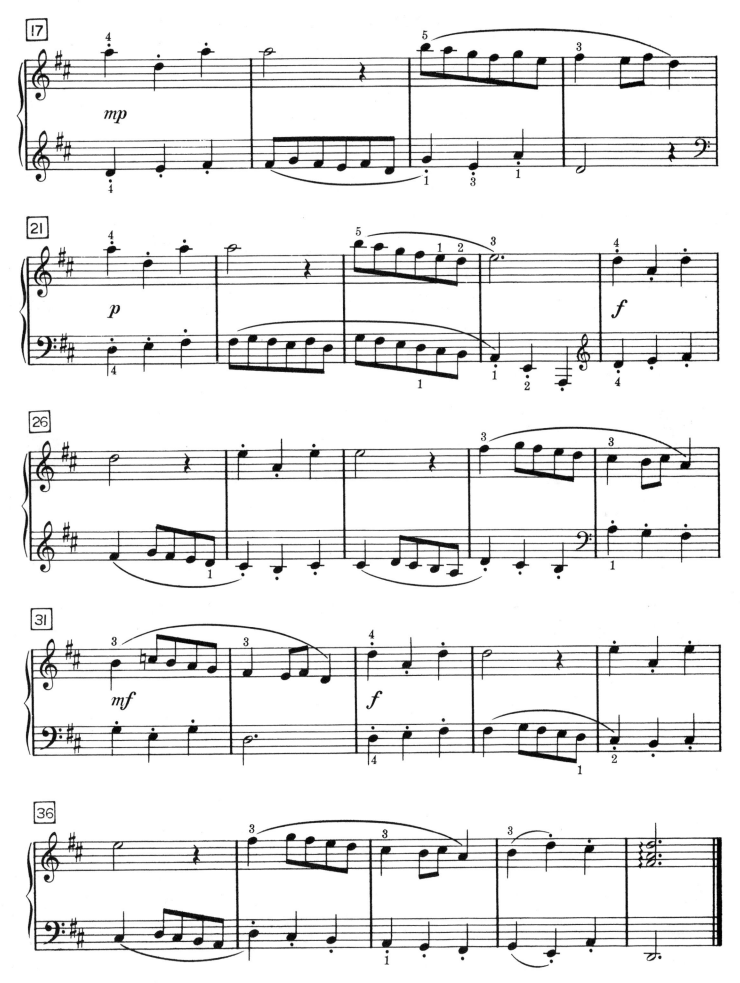

WP42

16 **Arcangelo Corelli (1653-1713)** was one of the leading Italian musicians of his time. He lived in Rome where he became famous as a violinist and composer. He is regarded as the founder of the modern violin technique, and pupils came from many countries to study with him.

Sarabande

Arcangelo Corelli

Jean Philippe Rameau (1683-1764) was a French organist and composer. He was also a great theorist, and his book *Treatise of Harmony* (1722) influenced later composers. Although he became famous for his operas, they are rarely performed today; however his charming miniature harpsichord pieces are performed frequently.

Minuet in Rondo Form

Allegretto

Jean Philippe Rameau

18 **George Frideric Handel (1685-1759)** was born in Halle, Germany, which was then the kingdom of Saxony. He was the son of a barber-surgeon who looked unkindly on music as a profession. To appease his father Handel studied law briefly while earning his livelihood as a church organist. Although he wrote forty operas, he became most famous for his oratorios, of which the best known, *The Messiah*, was written in twenty-four days! He founded the Royal Academy of Music in London. In addition to vocal music Handel wrote instrumental, organ, and keyboard music.

Minuet in F Major

George Frideric Handel

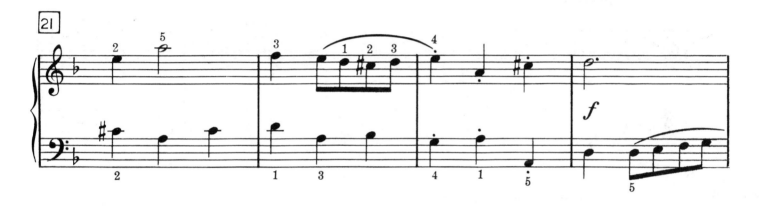

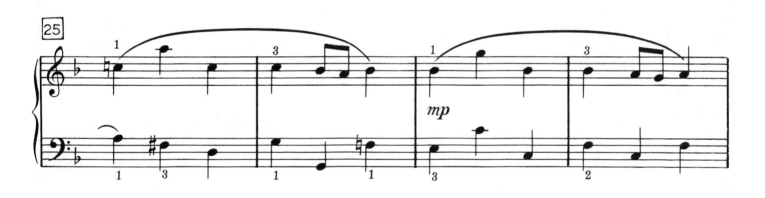

Sarabande and Variation

George Frideric Handel

Slow, stately

VARIATION

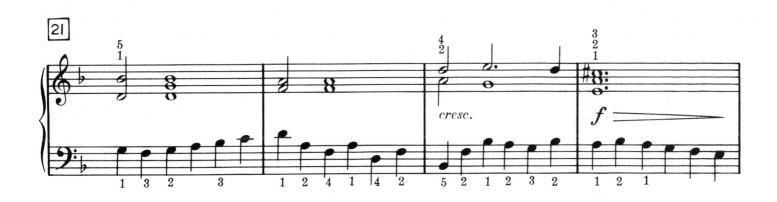

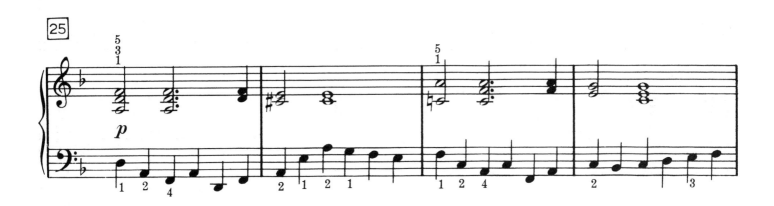

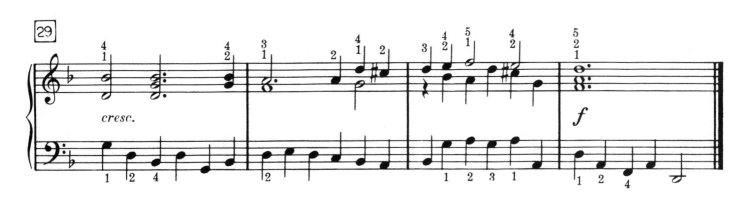

22 **Domenico Scarlatti (1685-1757)** was the son of the composer Alessandro Scarlatti. Although born and raised in Naples, Italy, Domenico spent most of his career in Madrid, Spain, under the patronage of Queen Maria Barbara. He wrote more than five hundred short pieces for the harpsichord. Although he titled most of these works sonatas, they are similar to brief etudes which use one particular technical device or figuration. His keyboard music is colorful and original and is played frequently in concert by harpsichordists and pianists.

Minuetto in C

Domenico Scarlatti

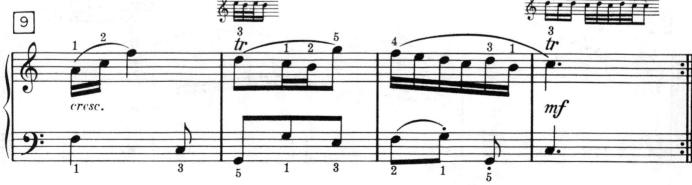

*The ornaments (trills) may be omitted in this piece if they are difficult for the student to play.

24 **Johann Sebastian Bach (1685-1750),** German composer, had numerous relatives who were musicians: from seven generations, 193 out of 200 were musicians. Bach's parents died when he was ten years old, and his oldest brother, Johann Christoph raised him. His brother died when Johann Sebastian was fifteen, and he lived at the St. Michael School where he studied music and was a choir boy. At nineteen, Bach obtained a position as organist at a church in Arnstadt. Throughout his life he held positions at various churches and in royal courts, and for almost thirty years he was director of music at the St. Thomas School in Leipzig. He was married twice and had twenty children, several of whom became well-known musicians. On his second wife's twenty-fifth birthday, he gave her (Anna Magdalena) a notebook containing pieces for members of his family to play. His best known easier clavier pieces come from this notebook. Bach was a prolific composer; his complete works fill forty-six large volumes containing choral music, concertos, orchestral and chamber works, and organ and clavier music.

Minuet in G Major (No. 1)

(from "Notebook for Anna Magdalena")

J. S. Bach

Minuet in G Minor

(from "Notebook for Anna Magdalena")

Allegretto

J. S. Bach

Musette in D Major

(from "Notebook for Anna Magdalena")

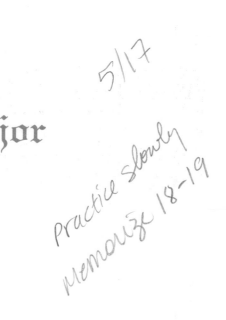

J. S. Bach

March in D Major

(from "Notebook for Anna Magdalena")

J. S. Bach

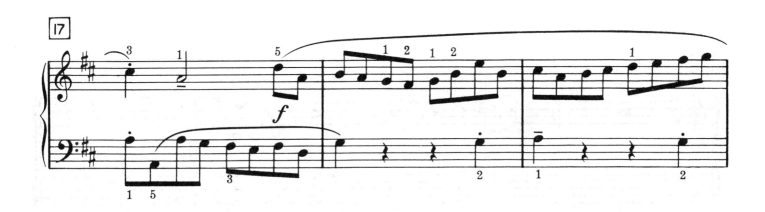

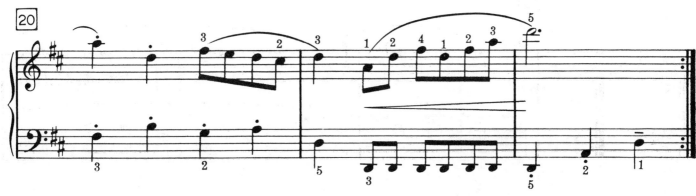

Minuet in D Minor

(from "Notebook for Anna Magdalena")

J. S. Bach

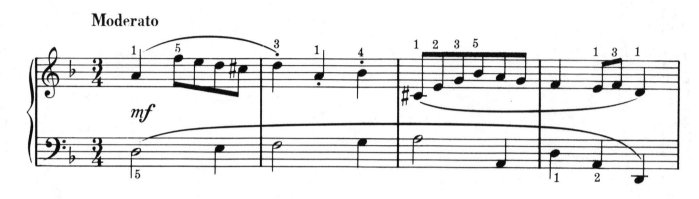

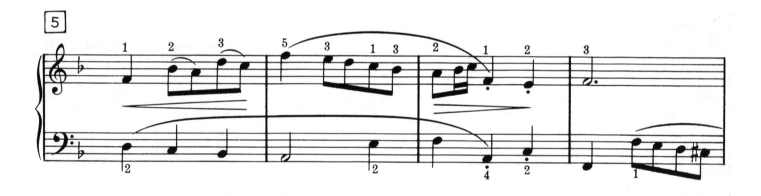

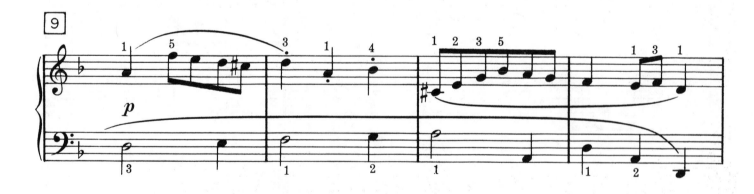

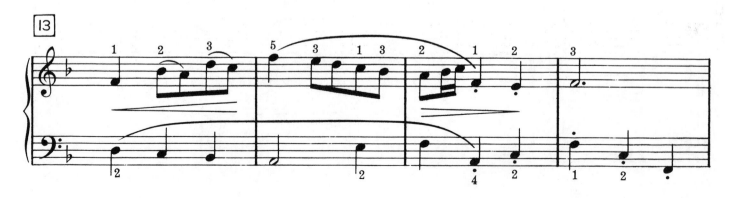

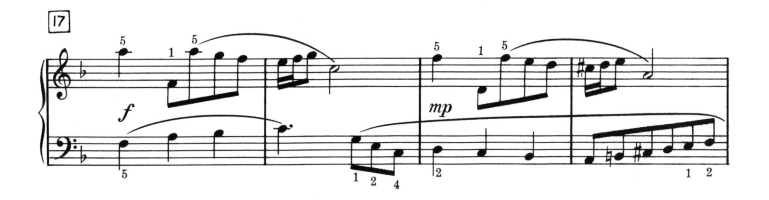

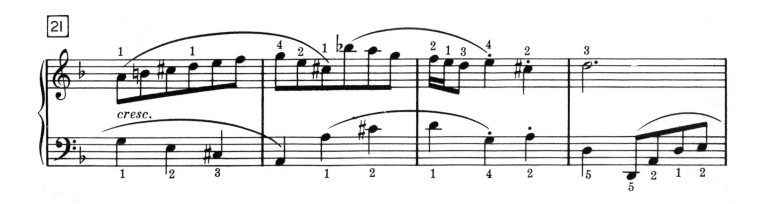

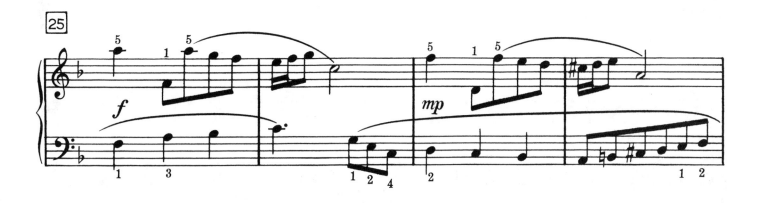

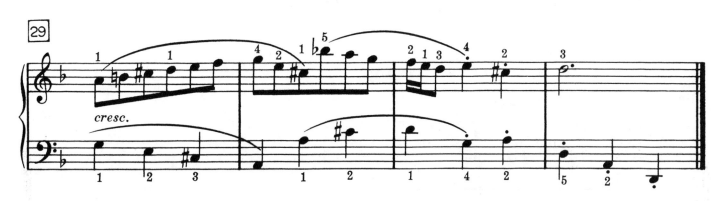

Minuet in G Major (No. 2)

(from "Notebook for Anna Magdalena")

J. S. Bach

Animato

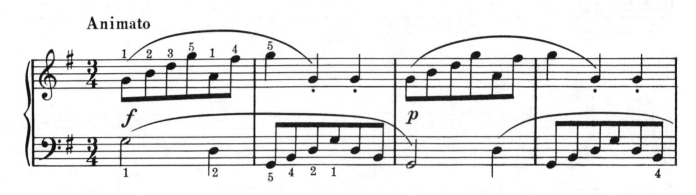

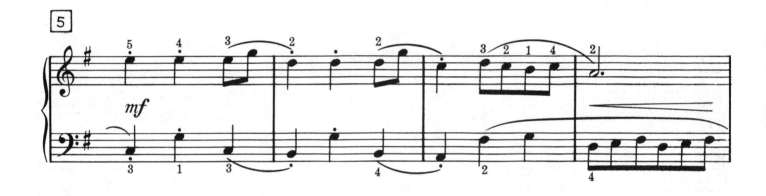

Prelude in C Major

(from "Twelve Short Preludes")

J. S. Bach

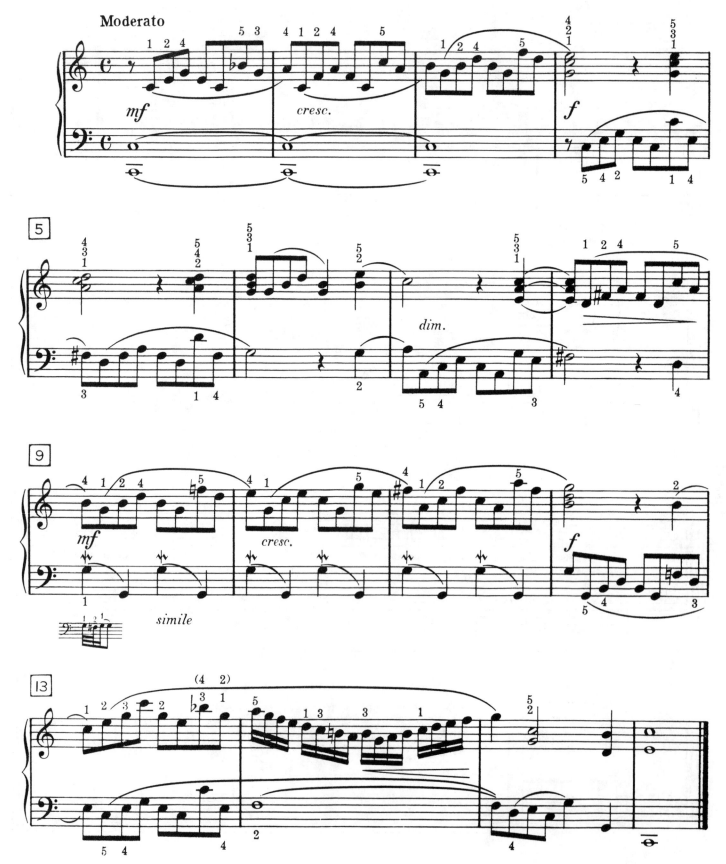

Musette

(from "English Suite No. 3 in G Minor")

J. S. Bach

Moderato

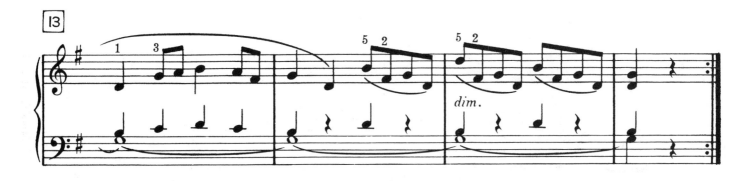

38

THE CLASSICAL
(1750-1820)

Italian pianoforte, by Bartolomeo Cristofori, 1720.
The Metropolitan Museum of Art, The Crosby Brown Collection of
Musical Instruments, 1889.

Square piano, made by Johannes Zumpe, London, 1770.
Courtesy Hugo Worch Collection, Smithsonian Institution.

Grand piano, made by Robert Stodart, London, 1790.
Courtesy Hugo Worch Collection, Smithsonian Institution.

PERIOD

The Early Piano

The possibilities of combining the sustaining tone of the clavichord with the power of the harpsichord were no doubt alluring to musicians and builders of the seventeenth century. It is not surprising that three inventors working independently in different countries perceived the hammer action piano concept about the same time: Cristofori in Italy (1709), Marius in France (1716), and Schröter in Germany (1717). Credit is given to Bartolomeo Cristofori, curator of musical instruments for the wealthy Medici family in Florence, for producing the first piano. Cristofori called his invention a *gravicembalo col piano e forte* (a keyboard instrument which can play soft and loud). The ability of the early piano to produce graded dynamics (crescendos and decrescendos), plus its light, silvery tone and sustaining quality appealed to composers and keyboard makers of the time.

By about 1728 Cristofori had improved his pianoforte by constructing a much stronger case than had been used for harpsichords, to withstand the increased strain of heavier strings. The action at this time resembled the basic mechanics of the modern piano: escapement device, a back check regulating the fall of the hammer, and a damper for each key.

Pianoforte building was continued by craftsmen such as Gottfried Silbermann (of Freiberg, Saxony, an organ builder who made pianofortes using Cristofori's and Schröter's actions), and Silbermann's pupils Johannes Zumpe and Americus Backers (Becker) who went to London to establish English pianoforte building. One of Silbermann's most talented pupils, Johann Stein, carried Viennese pianoforte making to new heights, and his instruments were preferred by Mozart (one of the first piano virtuosos), Beethoven, and others.

40 **Franz Joseph Haydn (1732-1809),** Austrian composer, as a youth studied singing, violin, and clavier and became a choirboy at the Vienna Cathedral. He spent more than thirty years in the service of Prince Esterhazy, a Hungarian nobleman, at Eisenstadt. Haydn was a major influence in the development of the symphony, sonata, and string quartet. During his long life he composed approximately eighty-three string quartets, more than fifty piano sonatas, two hundred songs, over one hundred symphonies, eighteen operas, a vast amount of church music, concertos, and many other works.

Minuet in G

Franz Joseph Haydn

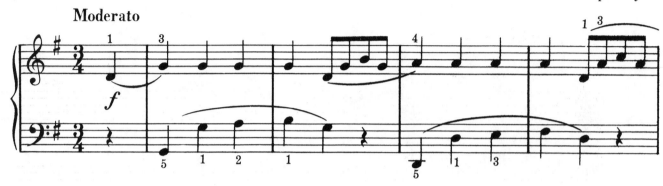

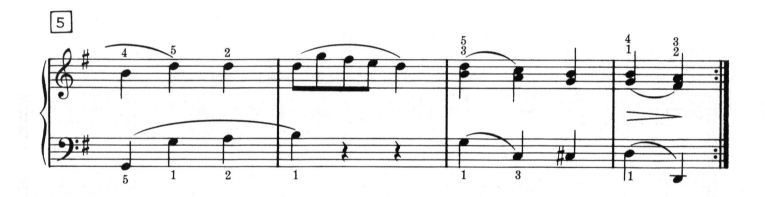

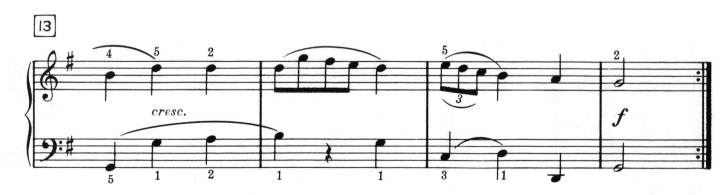

German Dance

Franz Joseph Haydn

Minuet in F Major

Franz Joseph Haydn

Scherzo

(from "Sonata No. 3")

Franz Joseph Haydn

Ignaz Pleyel (1757-1831) was a pianist, composer, and piano manufacturer. He lived and studied with Haydn from the age of fifteen to the age of twenty. Pleyel made several concert tours and founded a piano factory in 1807 in Paris which became one of the most famous in France. He was a prolific composer and his works, written in the style of Haydn, include string quartets, two piano concertos, symphonies, sonatas, and many pieces for piano.

Minuet

Ignaz Pleyel

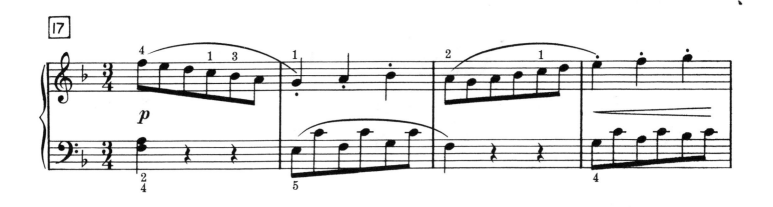

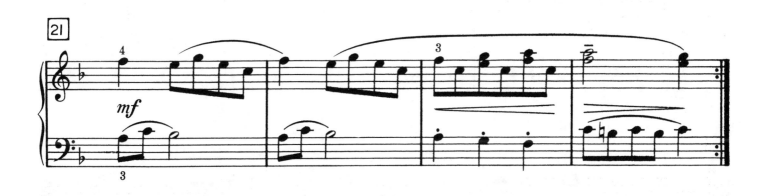

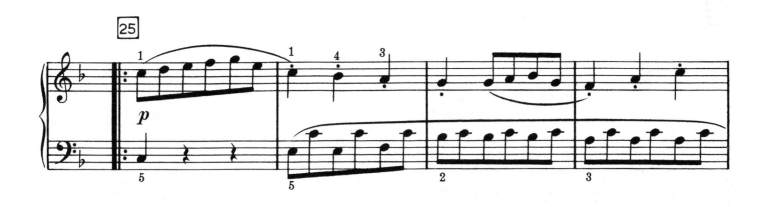

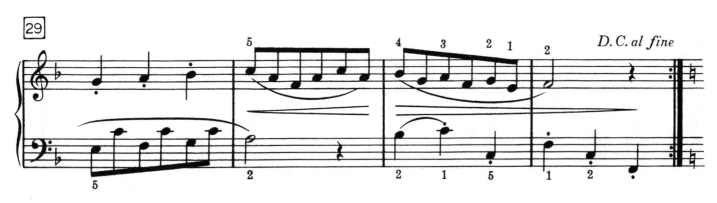

Wolfgang Amadeus Mozart (1756-1791), Austrian composer and pianist, was a child prodigy. He was taught how to play the harpsichord and violin by his father, Leopold, and by the age of five he could play and compose pieces. When he was six his father arranged a debut for Wolfgang and his sister. He was then exhibited all over Europe displaying his remarkable musical ability in performing, sight reading, improvising and playing his own compositions. Mozart could write a complete symphony during a stagecoach ride, or write out a complicated score from memory after one hearing. During his brief life, he wrote numerous symphonies, operas, concertos, songs, church music, chamber music, and keyboard music.

Minuet in C

(K.6)

Wolfgang Amadeus Mozart

Minuet in F

(K.2)

Wolfgang Amadeus Mozart

Minuet and Trio

(K.1)

Wolfgang Amadeus Mozart

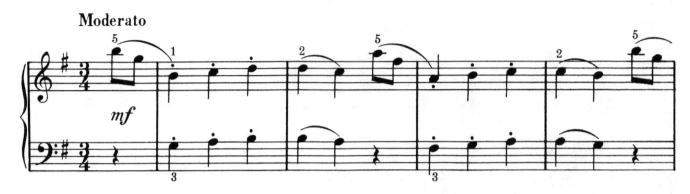

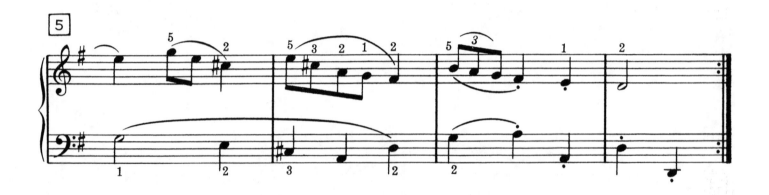

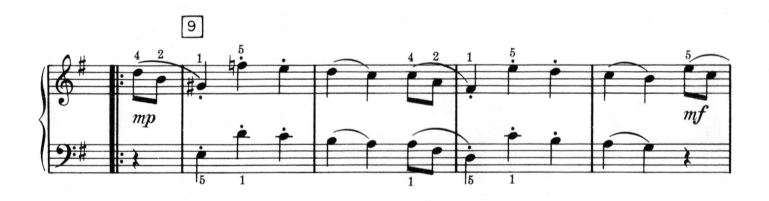

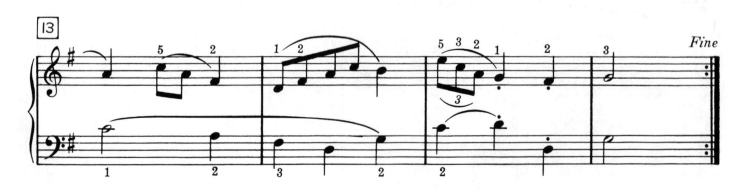

WP42

TRIO

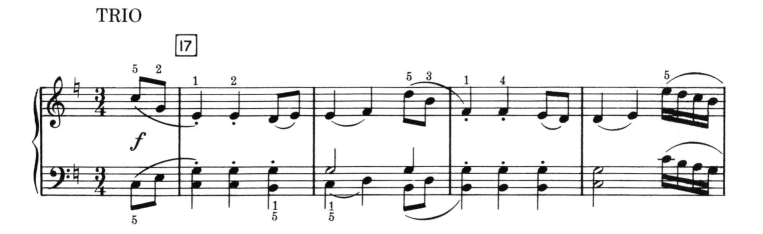

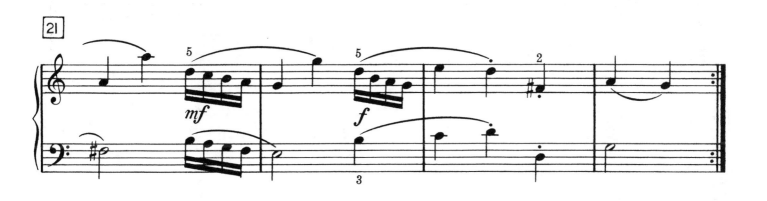

Minuet da capo

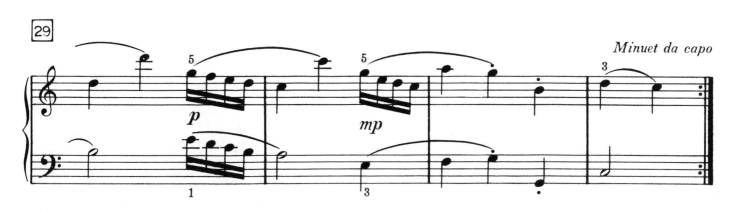

Allegro in B♭ Major

Wolfgang Amadeus Mozart

Anton Diabelli (1781-1858), Austrian composer and publisher, taught piano and guitar until he became owner of Diabelli and Company, his publishing firm. He published a large portion of Schubert's works. Beethoven wrote a set of variations on a theme by Diabelli which did a great deal to immortalize Diabelli's name.

Bagatelle

Anton Diabelli

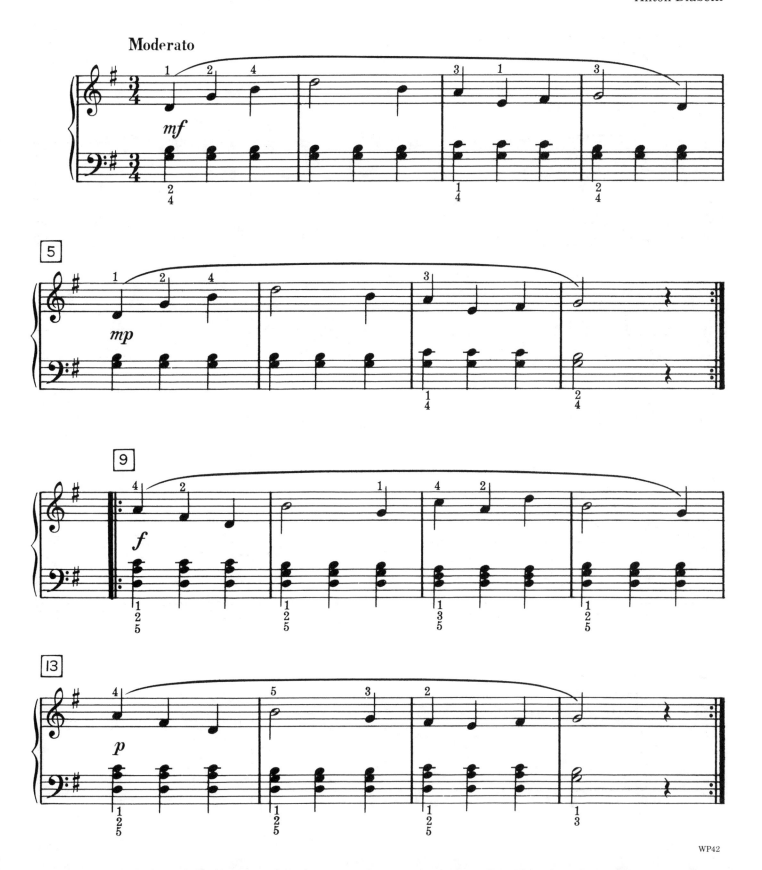

52 **Ludwig van Beethoven (1770-1827),** German composer, grew up in Bonn where he studied the violin and piano. Beethoven's father, a tenor employed as a chapel singer by the Archbishop-Elector of Bonn, was a stern taskmaster and drove young Ludwig to long hours of practice in hopes he would become a child prodigy like Mozart. Although Beethoven was obviously talented as a child, he did not develop into a marketable child prodigy. In 1787 he visited Vienna where he played for Mozart who predicted an outstanding musical career for him. Beethoven hurried back to Bonn to attend his mother who had•become ill. After his mother's death he remained five years at Bonn as a viola player in the court opera orchestra. In 1792 he returned to Vienna and studied with Haydn for about a year. About this time Beethoven began to earn his living from the sale of compositions and from teaching. He became an honored and respected musician to many royal families (Prince Lichnowsky, Count Waldstein, Count Rasumovsky, etc.), and many works were dedicated to these noblemen. In his early thirties Beethoven experienced hearing loss which later resulted in total deafness. Increasing deafness altered his character, and he grew morose and suspicious and had frequent outbursts of temper. A prolific composer, Beethoven wrote thirty-two piano sonatas, five piano concertos, one violin concerto, an opera, a great quantity of chamber music, and many other works.

Russian Folk Song

Ludwig van Beethoven

Ecossaise in G

Ludwig van Beethoven

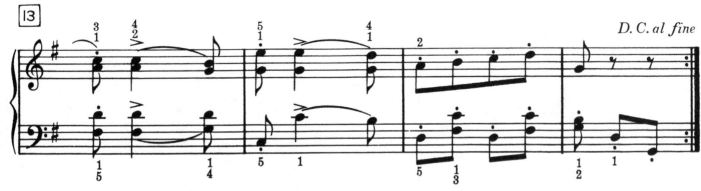

Für Elise*

Ludwig van Beethoven

*Although the original piece is written in sixteenth notes, the resultant sound is the same.

Sonatina in G

Ludwig van Beethoven

Romanze

Allegretto

60 **Muzio Clementi (1752-1832)** was a famous Italian pianist, composer, and teacher. In 1781 he and Mozart had a contest to determine which one was the better pianist. Although no winner was announced, Clementi was thought to have a better technique, but the audience felt that Mozart was a finer musician. Clemente wrote *The Art of Playing on the Piano-Forte* which he used with his beginning students. Chopin also used this book with his students. In addition to his teaching, composing, and performing, Clementi established a successful piano factory and a publishing company.

Sonatina, Op. 36, No. 1

Muzio Clementi

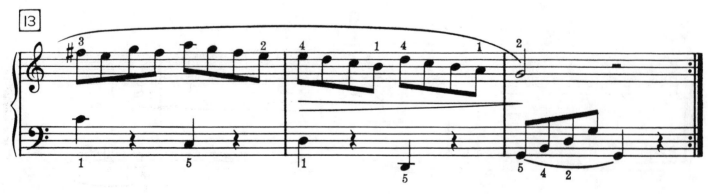

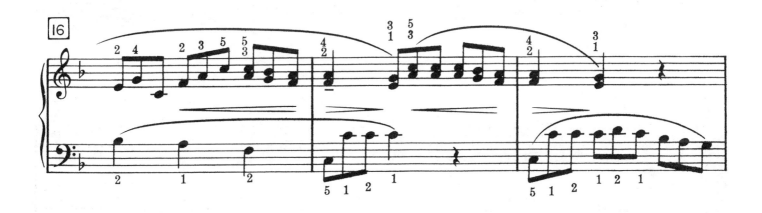

Rondo

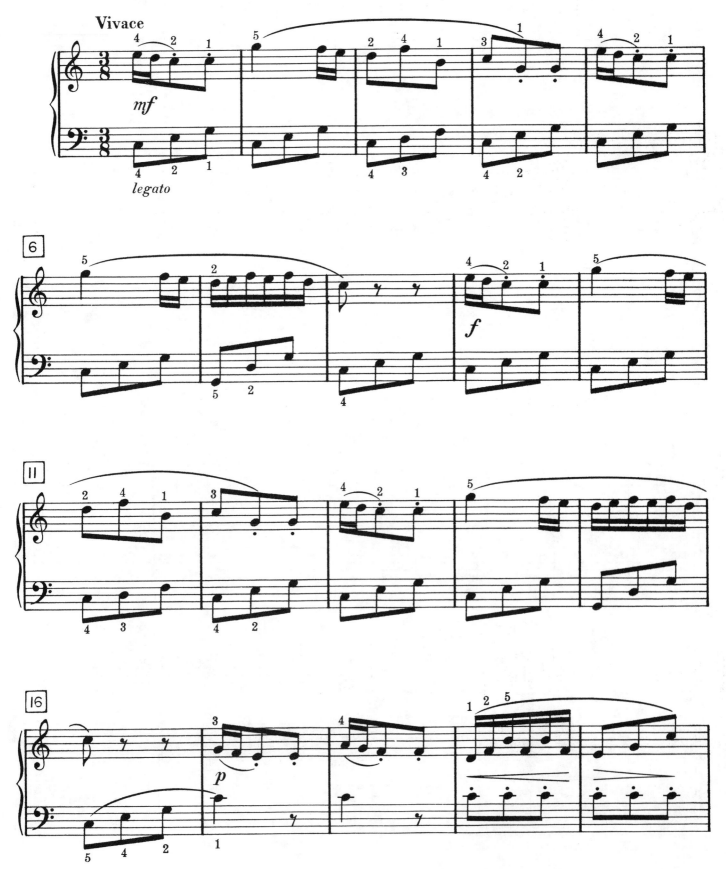

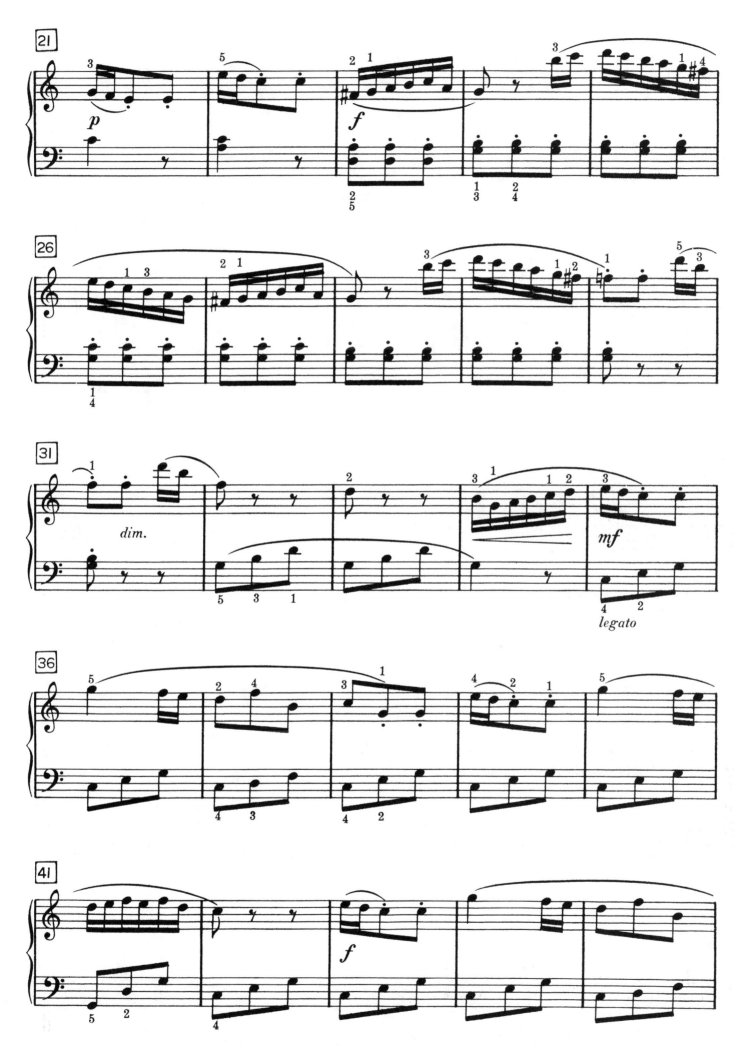

66

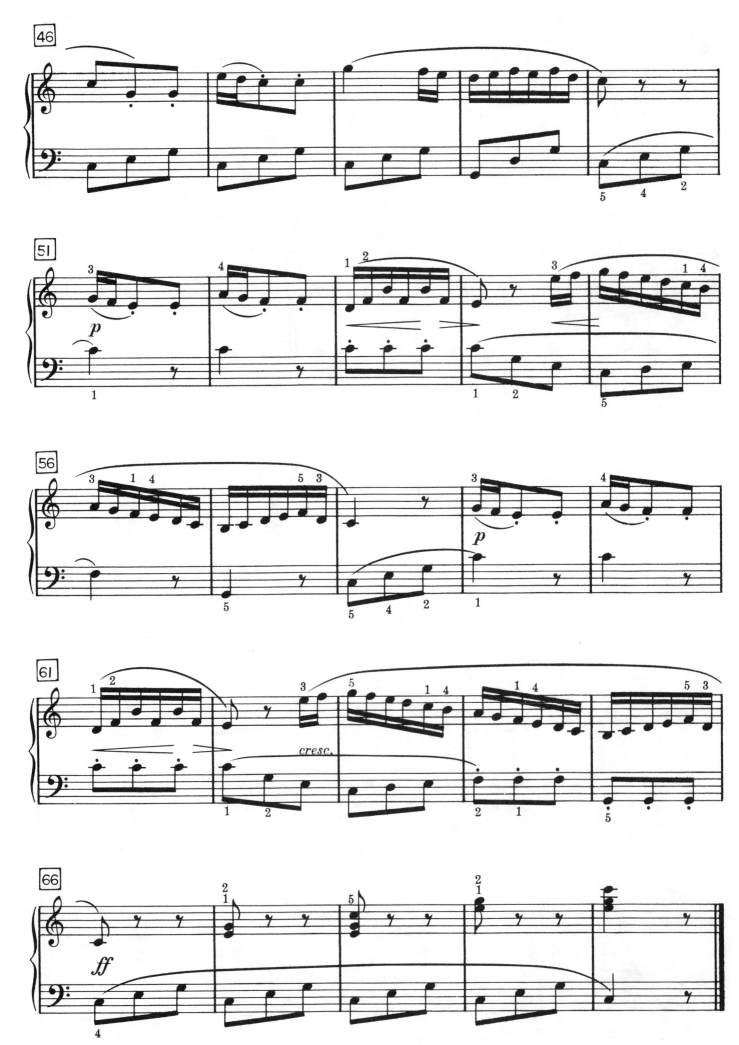

THE ROMANTIC
(1820-1900

English grand pianoforte, by John Broadwood, c. 1792.
The Metropolitan Museum of Art, Gift of Mr. and Mrs. Jerome C. Neuhoff, 1957.

The Development of the Pianoforte

The early pianofortes were small and produced light, delicate tones. Mozart's piano had a range of not quite five octaves. A pianoforte built by Broadwood in 1817 for Beethoven had a range of six octaves. It is interesting to note that J. S. Bach played one of Silbermann's pianofortes, and although he praised its tone, he complained that it was too weak in the treble, and it was too hard to play (stiff action). Beethoven thought the pianoforte was a German invention, and he called it the *hammerklavier*.

The period of 1760 to 1830 was one of great activity in the development of the pianoforte. Builders experimented with varying shapes, materials, and mechanisms. John Broadwood of London built a square piano in 1771 which he later improved to give it more tone. Some square pianos were fitted with drawers and book shelves and became popular parlor instruments. The French pianoforte builders, Sébastien and Pierre Érard, developed an instrument with a greater tone using a larger sound board (1776 – 1777).

By the end of the eighteenth century the pianoforte superseded the harpsichord, and composers wrote music for the "new" instrument. Until 1800 music was printed with the instruction "to be played on the harpsichord or pianoforte." Beethoven's first eight sonatas bore this indication.

English grand pianoforte, by John Broadwood and Sons, c. 1827.
The Metropolitan Museum of Art, Gift of Prof. Stoddard Lincoln, 1972.

PERIOD

English grand pianoforte, c. 1830.
The Metropolitan Museum of Art, Gift of Mrs. Henry McSweeney, 1959.

American mahogany piano, by John Tallman, New York, c. 1825.
The Metropolitan Museum of Art, The Crosby Brown Collection of Musical Instruments, 1889.

American rosewood piano, by Nunns and Clarke, c. 1850. Case decorated with Medallion of Queen Victoria and Prince Consort.
The Metropolitan Museum of Art, Gift of George Lowther, 1906.

70   **Franz Schubert (1797-1828),** Austrian composer, began violin lessons when he was eight. He was also given lessons on the piano, organ, composition, and in singing. He became a lead singer in the church choir in his tenth year. He followed his father's occupation as a teacher in an elementary school and taught unsuccessfully for three years from the age of sixteen to nineteen. During these years he devoted his leisure time to composing songs, and in one year alone (1815) he composed 144 songs. He struggled continually to make a living, and although he was a recognized as a composer of genius, he failed to obtain employment which would have provided a stable income. His income from compositions was limited. He was disgracefully underpaid by his publishers, and he lived mostly in extreme poverty. Schubert, who had a great melodic gift, is the acknowledged creator of the Romantic art song *(lied)*, and he wrote over six hundred songs *(lieder)*. He also wrote nine symphonies (including the famous "Unfinished" Symphony), religious works, choral music, operas, chamber music, and numerous piano solo and duet works.

Waltz in C

Franz Schubert

Waltz in A

Franz Schubert

72 **Robert Schumann (1810-1856),** German composer, was a child prodigy who played the piano when he was six years old and composed his first piano pieces when he was seven. His mother hoped he would become a lawyer, but he chose a music career and was allowed to study with the famous piano teacher, Friedrich Wieck, in Leipzig. Schumann injured his hand in 1832 trying to gain a better technique by tying his fourth finger to strengthen it. Because a career as a pianist was not now possible, he devoted his energies to composition. In 1840 he married Clara Wieck (his piano teacher's daughter) against her father's wishes. Clara was a brilliant pianist who performed many of Schumann's works. Schumann wrote about other musicians as a critic in his magazine, *The New Music Journal*; he was the first to report the importance of Chopin and Brahms. In 1850 Schumann was appointed Musical Director for the city of Dusseldorf. He held that position until 1853 when signs of insanity (which had been evident as early as 1833) compelled him to resign. From 1854 he spent the remainder of his life in an asylum at his own request. His compositions include symphonies, many piano works, a piano concerto, chamber music, songs and choral works. The pieces which follow are from the *Album for the Young* which Schumann wrote in 1848 as a birthday gift for his eldest daughter, Marie, who was then just seven years old.

Soldiers' March

(from "Album for the Young," Op. 68)

Robert Schumann

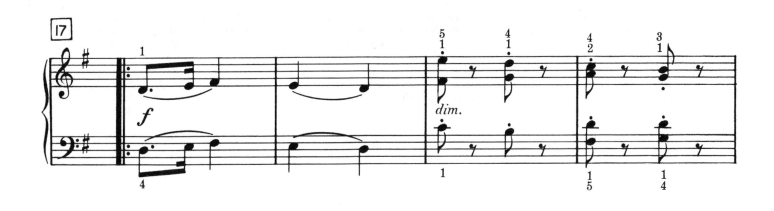

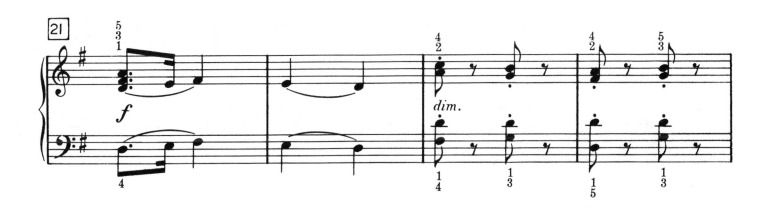

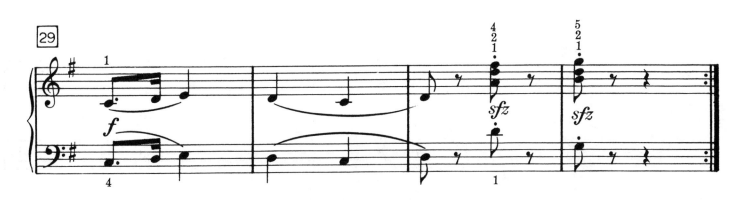

The Wild Horseman

(from "Album for the Young," Op. 68)

Robert Schumann

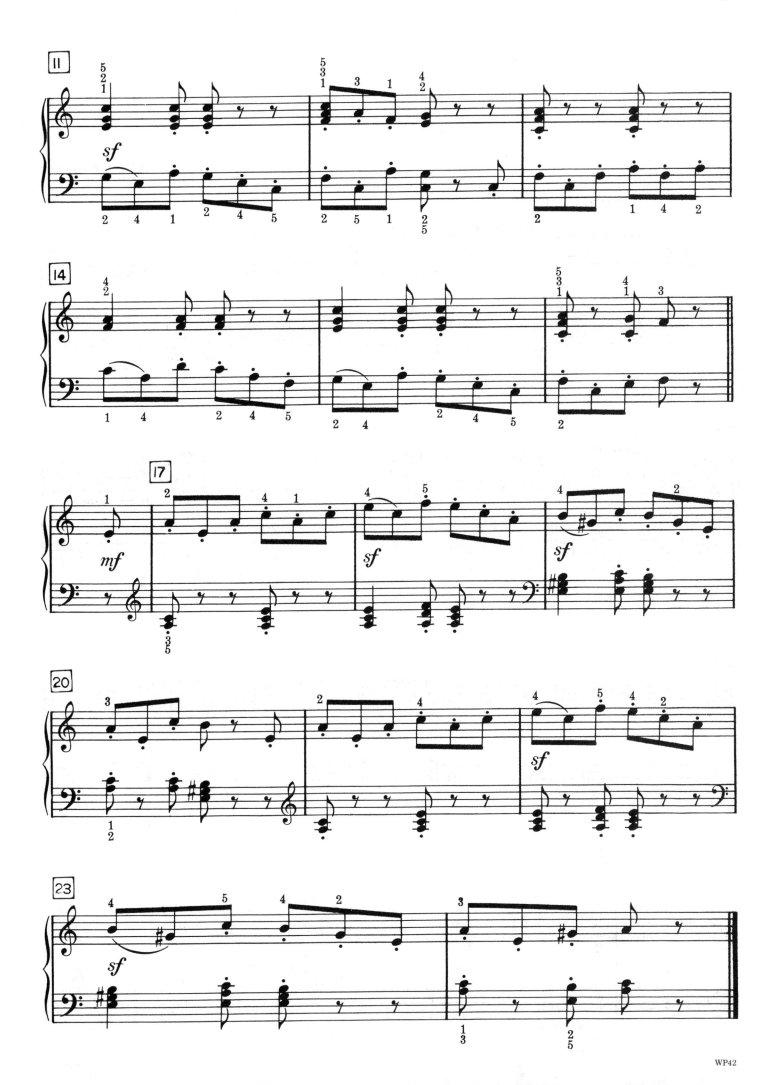

The Merry Farmer, Returning from Work

(from "Album for the Young," Op. 68)

Robert Schumann

Allegro animato

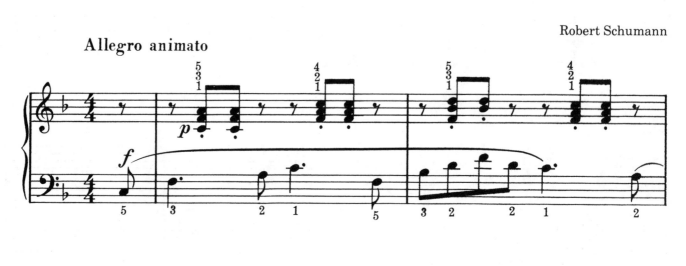

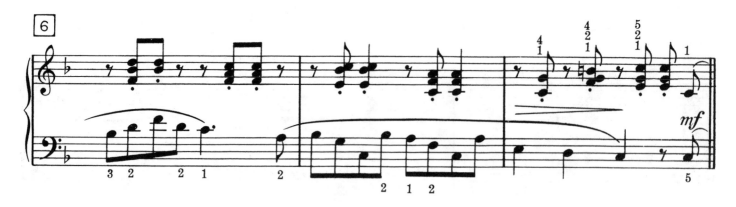

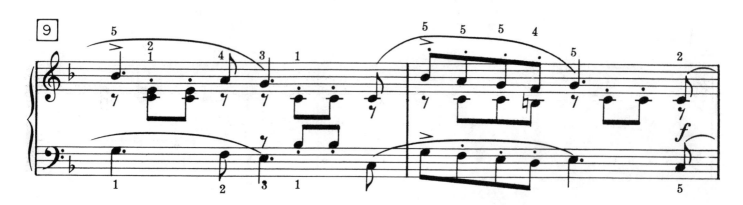

Little Song

(from "Album for the Young," Op. 68)

Robert Schumann

Sicilienne

(from "Album for the Young," Op. 68)

Robert Schumann

First Loss

(from "Album for the Young," Op. 68)

Robert Schumann

Andante con moto

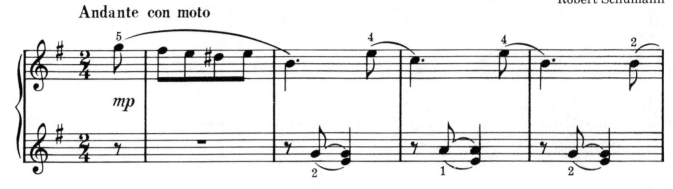

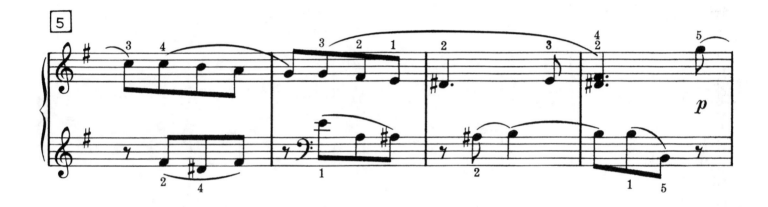

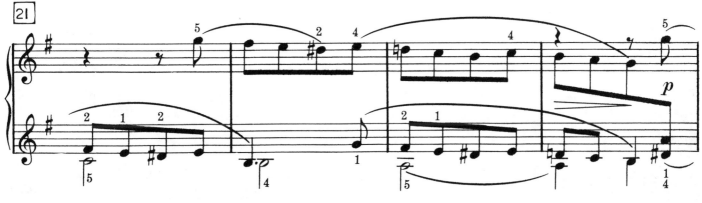

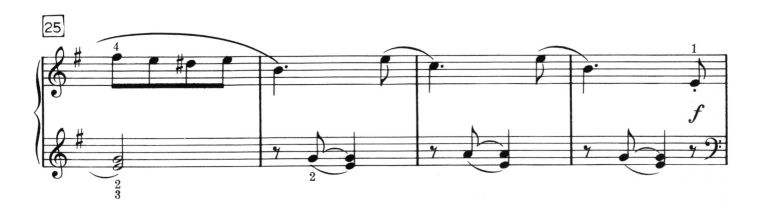

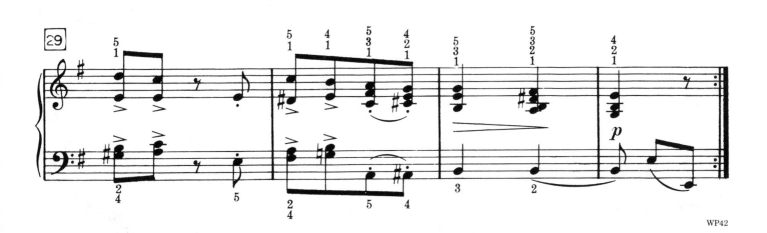

Hunting Song

(from "Album for the Young," Op. 68)

Robert Schumann

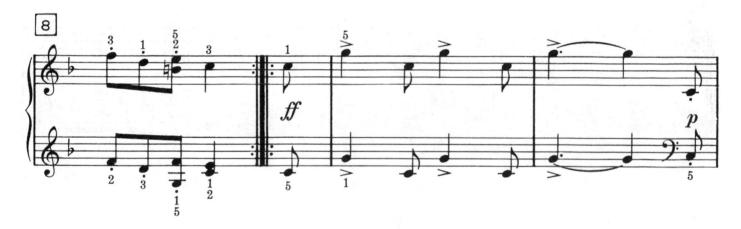

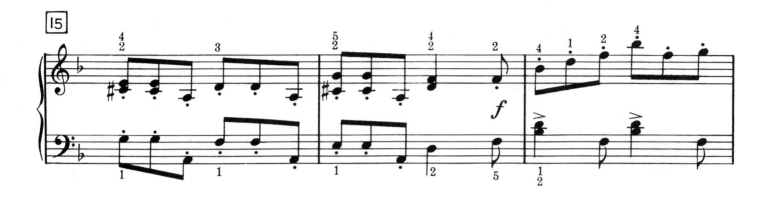

Felix Mendelssohn Bartholdy (1809-1847), German composer and pianist, was born in Hamburg of well-to-do parents. When Felix was three, his parents moved to Berlin where schooling began with private tutors. He first performed in public at the age of nine, and he began to compose at the age of twelve. He wrote his famous overture to *A Midsummer Night's Dream* when he was seventeen. He traveled extensively through England, Scotland, and the continent. His trips inspired him to write the descriptive overture *Fingal's Cave* and his *Symphony Number Three* ("Scotch") while in Scotland. A visit to Italy resulted in his *Symphony Number Four* ("Italian"). In 1829 Mendelssohn conducted J. S. Bach's *St. Matthew Passion* which was the first performance of a major work by Bach since his death almost eighty years earlier. The result was a revival of interest in Bach's music. Mendelssohn's interest in choral music inspired him to compose his oratorios *St. Paul* (1836) and for presentation in England, *Elijah* (1846). Mendelssohn was an extremely busy musician acting as a pianist, conductor of orchestras in Düsseldorf and Leipzig, and founder and dean of the Leipzig Conservatory, where he taught piano and composition. His health was never robust, and these taxing musical activities plus a whirl-wind social life strained his constitution severely, and he literally wore himself out and died of apoplexy at the age of thirty-eight. He was a prolific composer and worked in almost every medium except opera. His works include orchestral music, the *Violin Concerto in E Minor* (1844), piano concertos, choral and vocal music, chamber music, organ works, and well-known piano works such as the *Andante and Rondo Capricioso* op. 14, *Variations Sérieuses* op. 54, and eight books of *Songs Without Words*.

Romanze

Felix Mendelssohn

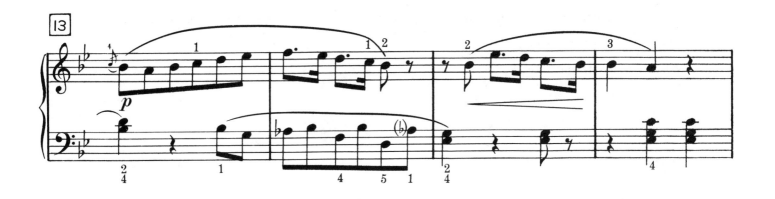

Johann Friedrich Franz Burgmüller (1806-1874), German composer, came from a musical family. Johann settled in Paris where he wrote and performed light salon pieces for the piano. His most famous piano teaching volume is his *25 Progressive Pieces, Op. 100.* The following two pieces are from that collection.

Arabesque

(from "25 Progressive Pieces," Op. 100)

Friedrich Burgmüller

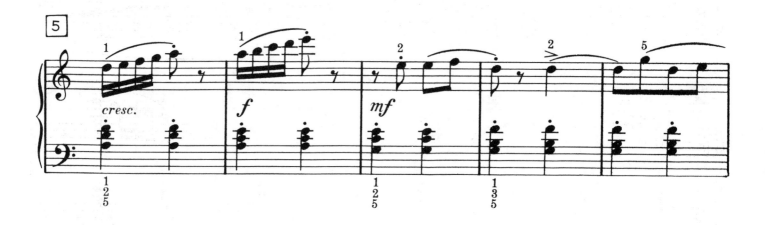

Ballade

(from "25 Progressive Pieces," Op. 100)

Friedrich Burgmüller

Allegro con brio

Cornelius Gurlitt (1820-1901), German composer, was a pianist and organist. Although he wrote extended works, such as operas and sonatas for various instruments, he is mainly remembered for his piano miniatures written in the style of Schumann's *Album for the Young*.

Morning Song

Cornelius Gurlitt

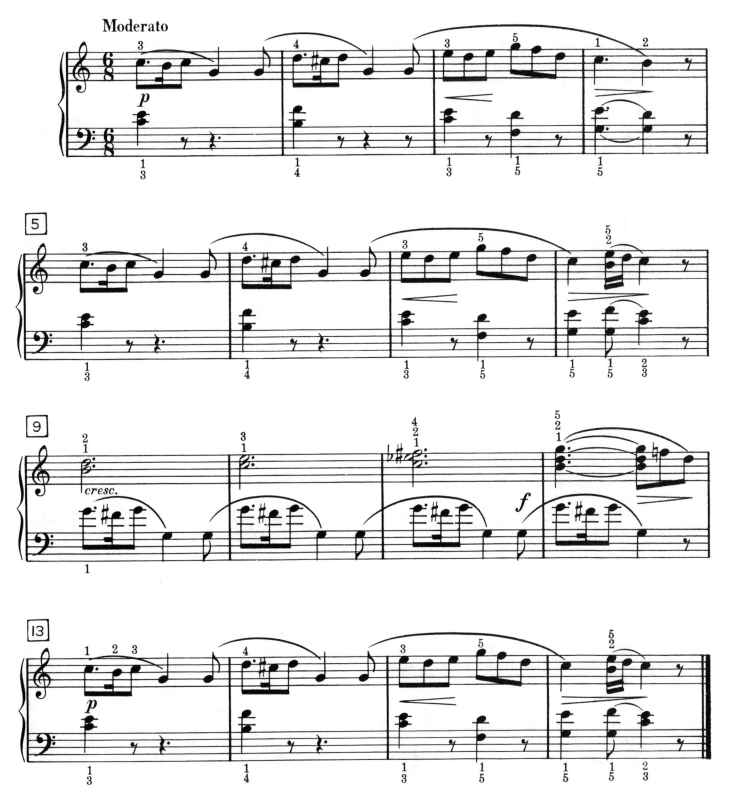

Carl Maria von Weber (1786-1826) was credited with founding the German Romantic style of composition. His father was an amateur musician and the director of a traveling dramatic company. Because of extensive travels with this company, Carl did not receive regular education, but he gained theater experience which influenced his direction toward dramatic composition. He wrote many operas, orchestral and choral music, songs, two piano concertos, chamber music, and piano music.

Scherzo

Carl Maria von Weber

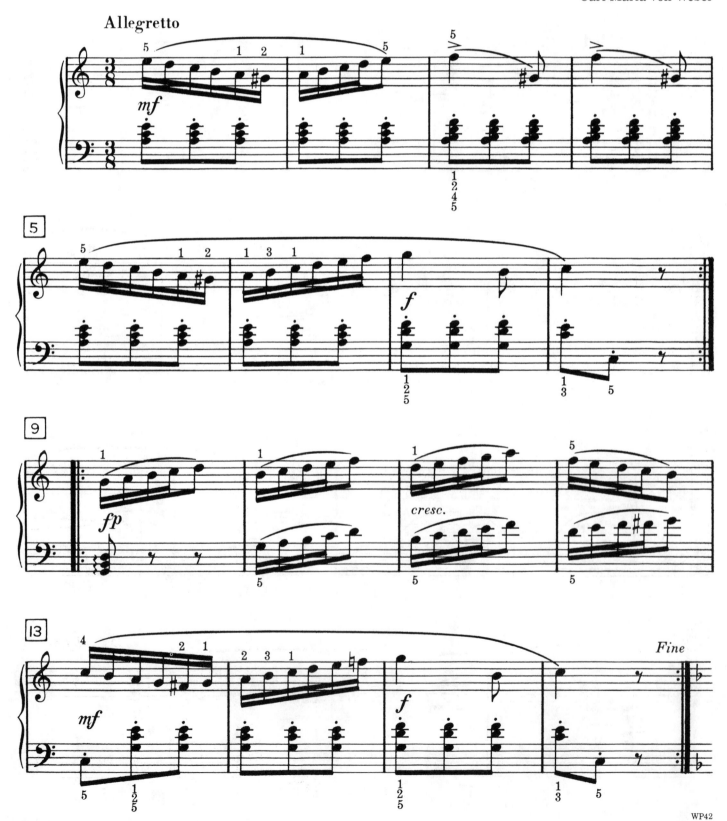

TRIO

D.C. al fine

94 **Peter Ilyich Tchaikovsky (1840-1893),** Russian composer, showed no special musical talent when he was young, but at the age of twenty-one he began to study with Anton Rubinstein at the Moscow Conservatory. Tchaikovsky became a Professor of harmony at the Conservatory when he was twenty-six. He was supported through financial difficulties by Madame Von Meck, a wealthy widow whom he never met. The security of the stipend he received from her enabled him to compose a great quantity of music. He traveled widely, even to America in 1891 where he was well received as a composer. His works include the ballets *Swan Lake, The Sleeping Beauty*, and *The Nutcracker; the Piano Concerto Number 1;* many orchestral works, choral music, chamber music, songs, and piano music. *The Doll's Funeral* and *Italian Folk Song* are from *Children's Album*, composed in 1878.

The Doll's Funeral

(from "Children's Album")

Peter Ilyich Tchaikovsky

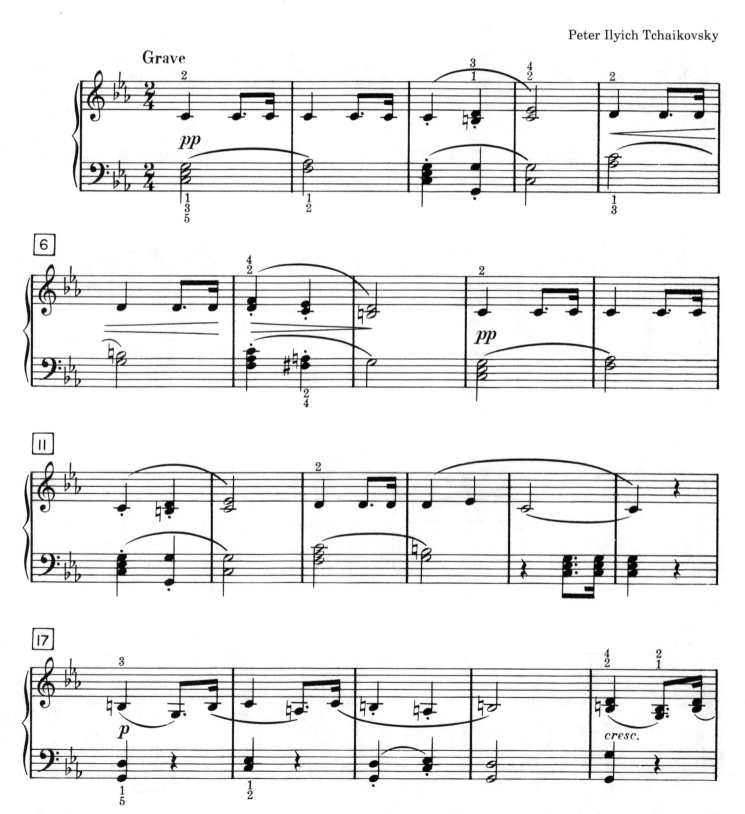

Italian Folk Song

(from "Children's Album")

Peter Ilyich Tchaikovsky

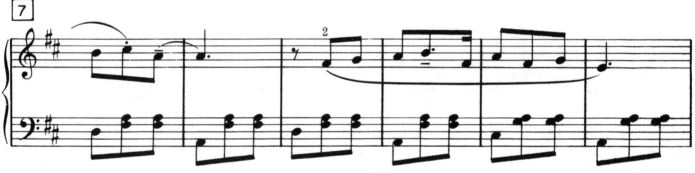

Edward MacDowell (1861-1908), American composer, studied in France and Germany. He remained in Germany until 1888 and then returned to America to live in Boston. In 1896 he began teaching at Columbia University and resigned eight years later in a bitter disagreement with the administration. His health began to fail, and he spent the last years of his life insane, unaware of his identity and his surroundings. Money was raised for him to live in comfort at Peterborough, New Hampshire, and after his death, the residence became a retreat for composers and writers. MacDowell's works include the famous second piano concerto, orchestral music, songs, and piano music. *To a Wild Rose* is from the album, *Woodland Sketches*, composed in 1896.

To A Wild Rose

(from "Woodland Sketches")

Edward MacDowell

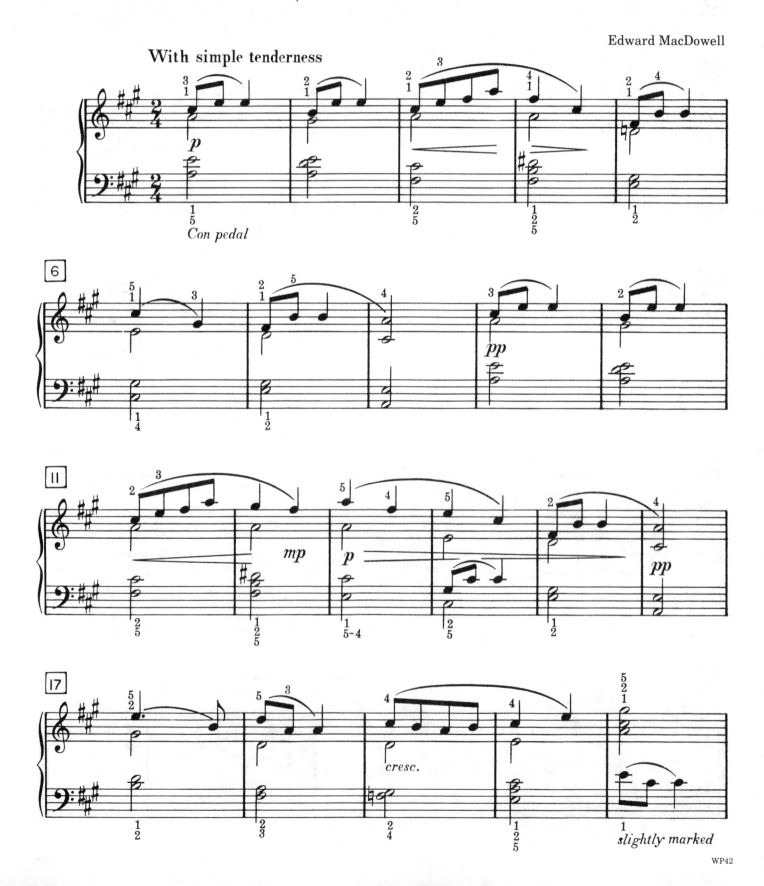

THE CONTEMPORARY

(1900-present

PIANO (Electronic)

A modern electronic piano manufactured in Germany by the firm of Hohner. Electronic keyboard instruments have achieved an especially wide acceptance in the fields of popular music and class piano instruction during the mid-20th century.

PERIOD

PIANO (20th Century)

A modern Bosendorfer Concert Grand (Austrian manufactured) awaiting an audience in the Royal Festival Hall, London.

Dmitri Kabalevsky (1904-   ), Russian composer, was born in St. Petersburg, now called Leningrad. He began to play the piano by ear when he was six years old, but he did not begin formal lessons until he was fourteen. At that time his family moved to Moscow, and he entered the Scriabin School of Music studying piano and composition. When he was twenty-one he entered the Moscow Conservatory and was such a brilliant student that upon graduation he was invited to become a Professor of Composition. In addition the Russian Government hired him to teach in the Scriabin School, and he wrote teaching materials for the children. Among the best known works for young students are his piano pieces *(Children's Pieces*, Op. 27; *24 Little Pieces for Children*, Op. 39; and *Variations*, Op. 40), and youth concertos (the best known being the *Youth Concerto for Piano, No. 3)*. In addition to composing and teaching Kabalevsky has been a conductor, music critic, musicologist, and has toured as a pianist. He has written many different kinds of music: symphonies, concertos, ballets, chamber music, advanced piano pieces, and has also written music for radio programs, movies, and stage plays.

Little Dance

(from "24 Little Pieces For Children," Op. 39)

Dmitri Kabalevsky

Follow The Leader

(from "24 Little Pieces For Children," Op. 39)

Dmitri Kabalevsky

The Clown

(from "24 Little Pieces For Children," Op. 39)

Dmitri Kabalevsky

Toccatina

(from "Children's Pieces," Op. 27)

Dmitri Kabalevsky

Sonatina

(from "Children's Pieces," Op. 27)

Dmitri Kabalevsky

110 **Aram Khatchaturian (1903-1978),** Russian composer, studied cello and composition at the Gniessin School in Moscow when his parents moved there from Tiffis when he was seventeen. He graduated from the Moscow Conservatory in 1934 and developed rapidly as a composer writing such frequently played works as the *Violin Concerto, Toccata* (piano), and the *Sabre Dance* from his ballet, *Gayane*.

Ivan Sings

(from "Children's Pieces")

Aram Khatchaturian

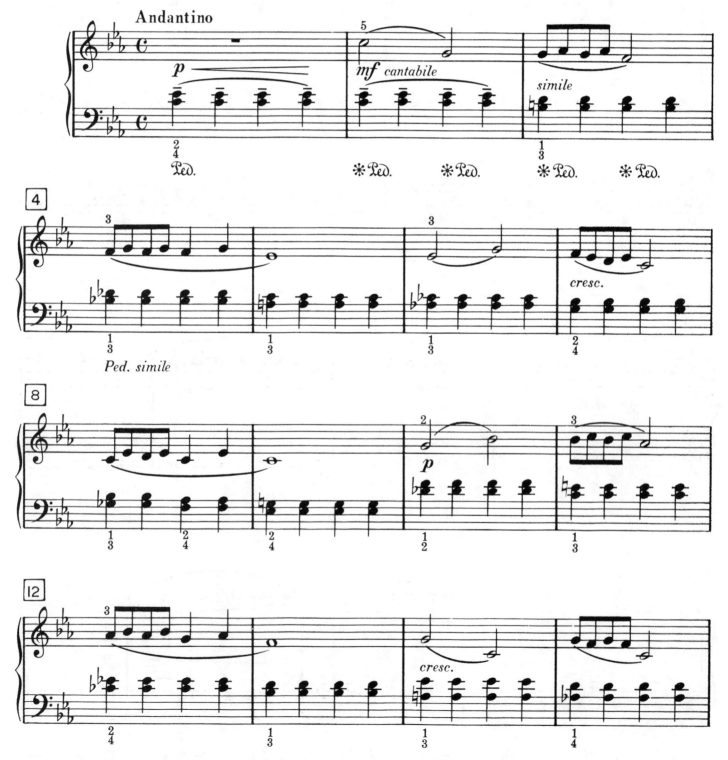

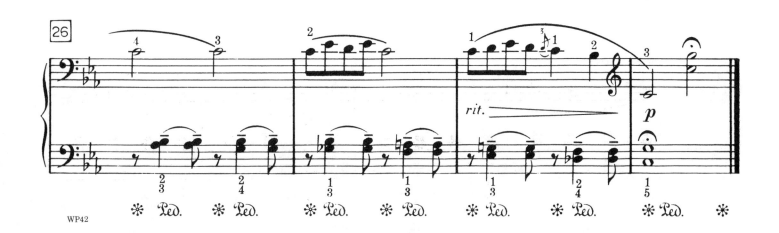

WP42

Béla Bartók (1881-1945), Hungarian composer, studied the piano with his mother as a child. He completed his musical training at the Franz Liszt Academy in Budapest studying piano with Istvan Thoman, who had been a pupil of Liszt. Bartók was a brilliant pianist, and he made concert tours throughout Europe and to America in 1927. He returned to Budapest where he was a Professor of Piano at the Conservatory. Because of political difficulties, he came to the United States in 1940 where he lived until his death. He spent many years collecting Hungarian and Slavic folk music, much of which is reflected in his music. He wrote more than one hundred piano pieces for youngsters in collections such as *First Term at the Piano, For Children*, and *Ten Easy Pieces*. His works include advanced piano music, orchestral works, concertos, choral music, chamber music, songs, and music for the stage.

Sad Song

(from "For Children")

Béla Bartók

Hungarian Folk Song

(from "For Children")

Béla Bartók

Follow The Leader

(from "For Children")

Béla Bartók

Allegretto

A little faster

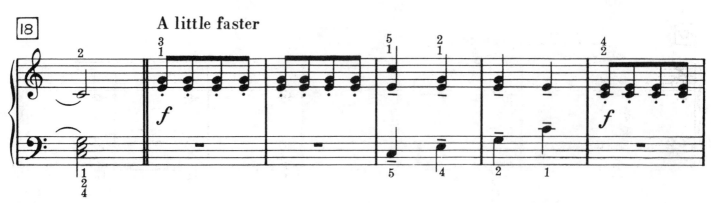

Folk Dance

(from "For Children")

Béla Bartók

sempre stacc.

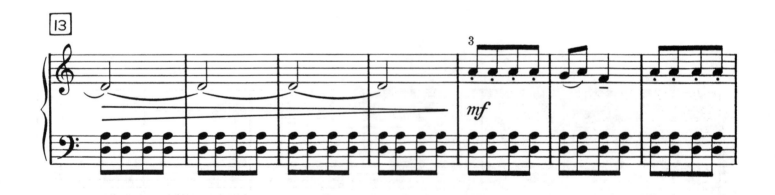

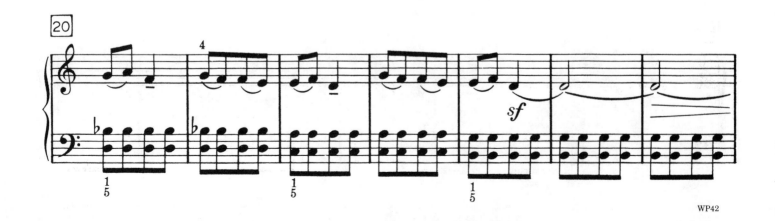

The Weary Traveler

Béla Bartók

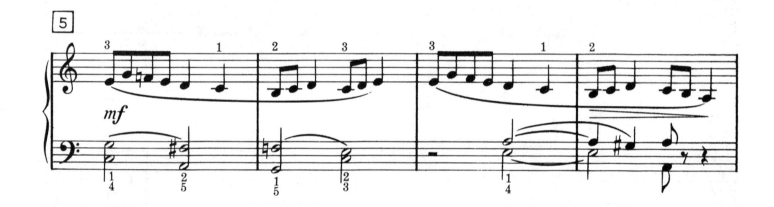

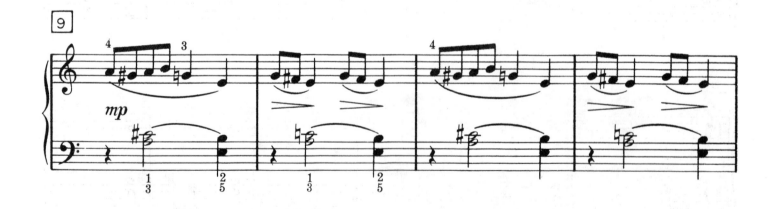

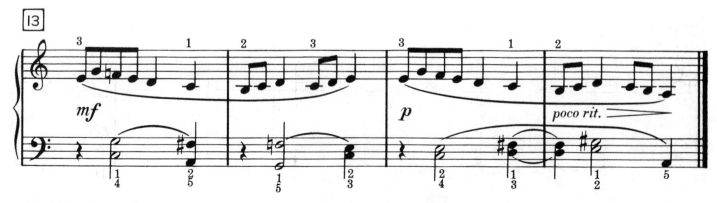

Springtime Song

(from "For Children")

Béla Bartók

120 **Dmitri Shostakovich (1906-1975),** Russian composer, studied at the St. Petersburg Conservatory. He wrote his first symphony at the age of eighteen as a graduation piece, and it became his most frequently performed work. He wrote music of all kinds: symphonies, ballets, chamber music, operas, choral music, concertos, songs, piano music, and film scores. The *Polka* from the ballet *The Golden Age* (1930) is one of his best known works. "March" and "Waltz" are from *Six Children's Pieces* which he wrote for his daughter.

March

(from "Six Children's Pieces")

Dmitri Shostakovich

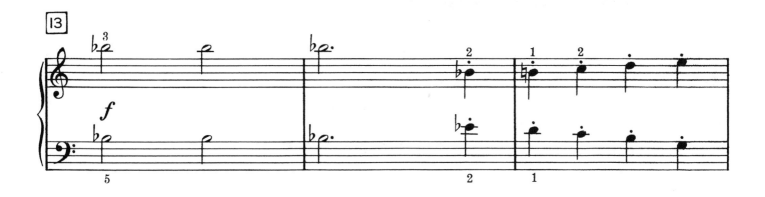

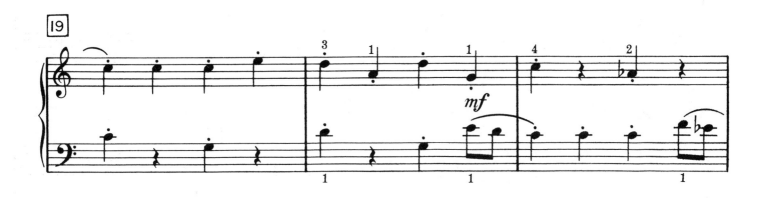

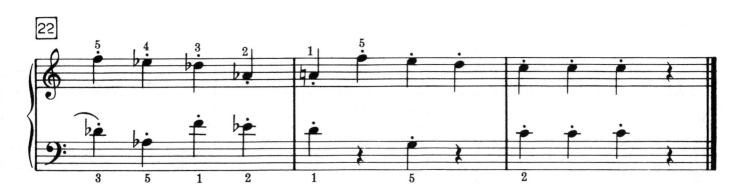

Waltz (In A Minor)

(from "Six Children's Pieces")

Dmitri Shostakovich

Tempo di valse

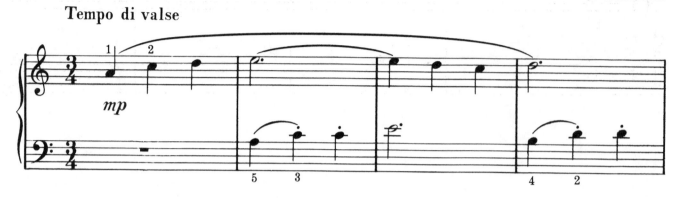

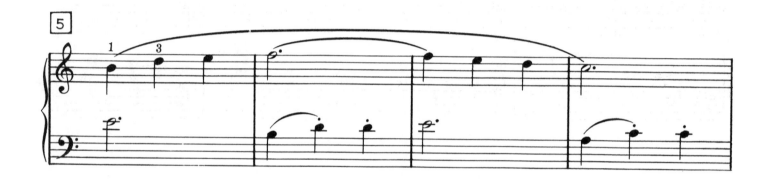

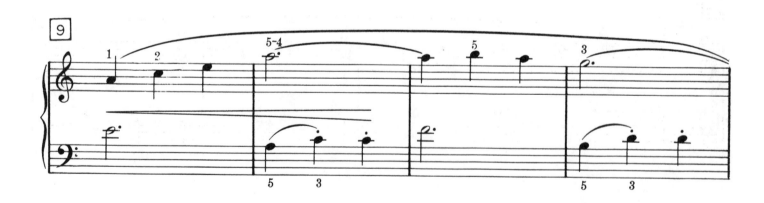

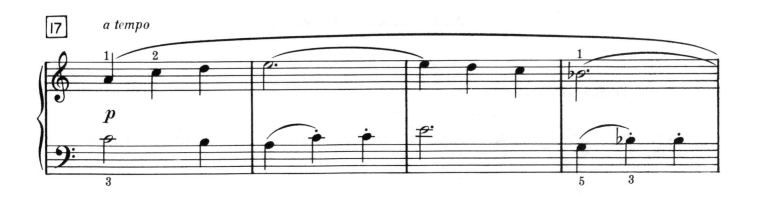

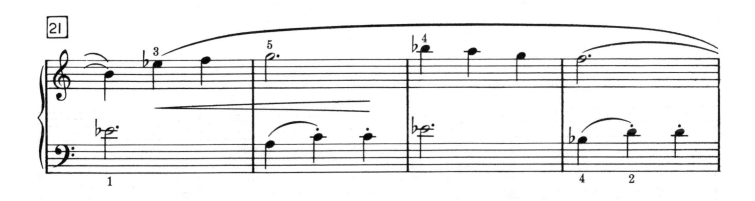

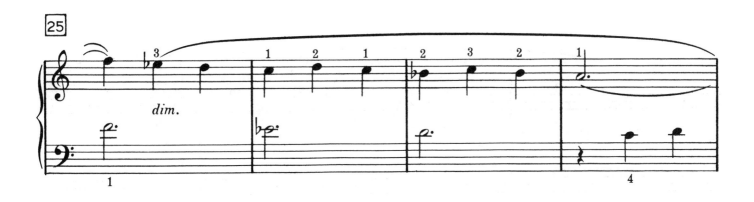

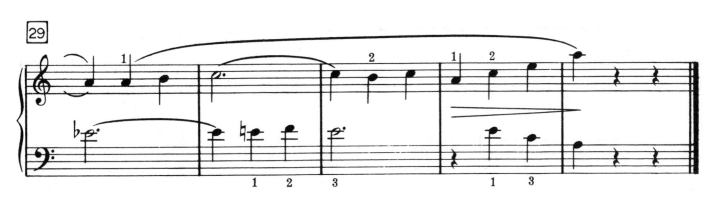

ARRANGEMENTS

A piano arrangement frequently is an adaptation of a composition written for another medium; or it may be an adaptation of a piano work. Some piano arrangements are for study purposes, such as arrangements of symphonies, operas, chamber music, etc. Other piano arrangements are intended for performance, and in these the arranger may be more creative, reworking, adding to, or abbreviating the original work.

Numerous composers have made arrangements of other composers' works or arrangements of their own compositions. Bach arranged violin concertos by Vivaldi and other composers for the harpsichord and organ. Haydn's *The Seven Last Words* was originally written as an instrumental suite and was also arranged as a string quartet and as a choral work. Beethoven made a piano concerto arrangement of his violin concerto. Liszt made numerous concert arrangements of Bach works, Schubert songs, and opera themes by various composers (Bellini, Gounod, Mendelssohn, Mozart, Rossini, Verdi, and Wagner). Brahms arranged his orchestral piece *Variations on a Theme by Haydn* for two pianos, and arranged his *Sonata for Two Pianos* for *Piano Quintet*. Brahms also made a simplified piano arrangement of his *Sixteen Waltzes, Op. 39*. Mussorgsky's piano work *Pictures at an Exhibition* was later arranged for orchestra by Ravel.

Performers such as Bussoni, Rachmaninoff, Horowitz, and many others have made stunning concert arrangements of other composers' works. The famous conductor Leopold Stokowski arranged Bach's organ work *Toccata and Fugue in D Minor* for orchestra.

Arrangements provide an accessibility of master composers' music and serve to acquaint the student with a wide spectrum of music for various mediums. Before the advent of recorded sound, arranged works were used to acquaint the musician with symphonies, chamber music, etc. In many instances arrangements have helped to promote an awareness of composers' works which otherwise might not have been as well known.

"Surprise" Symphony

(Theme from 1st Movement)

Joseph Haydn

arr. by James Bastien

Andante

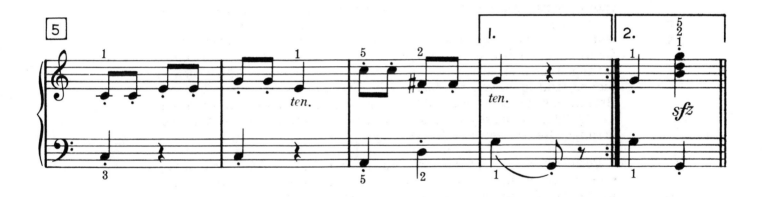

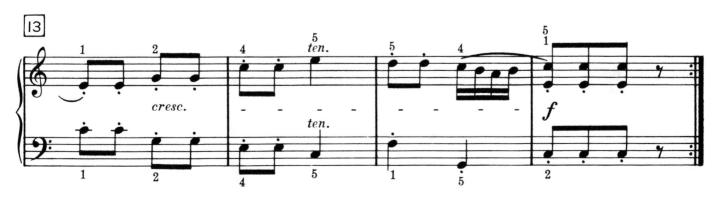

126 **Antonin Dvořák (1841-1904),** Bohemian composer, learned to play the violin as a child, and at the age of sixteen he entered the Prague Organ School. He earned a precarious living as an orchestral musician (violin and viola). In 1873 he was appointed organist at a church in Prague, and he became Professor of Composition at the Prague Conservatory. For a three-year period he was the director of the National Conservatory of Music in New York. He lived briefly in Spillville, Iowa, where he worked on his famous *Symphony in E Minor* ("From the New World"). Many of his works have a nationalistic flavor (*Slavonic Dances, Rhapsodies*, etc.). His compositions include symphonies, operas, concertos (violin, piano, cello), choral music, chamber music, vocal, and piano music.

New World Symphony

(Theme from 2nd Movement)

Antonin Dvořák

arr. by James Bastien

"Pathetique" Symphony

(Theme from 1st Movement)

Peter Ilyich Tchaikovsky

arr. by James Bastien

128 **Camille Saint-Saëns (1835-1921),** French composer, began the study of piano as a child and made such rapid progress that at the age of eleven he made his debut playing concertos by Mozart and Beethoven. He studied at the Paris Conservatory where he won first prize for organ. He was acclaimed as an organ virtuoso and was regarded as a master of improvisation. An accomplished pianist, he traveled widely as a pianist and conductor to the U.S., South America, Greece, etc. His works include concertos (piano, violin, cello), chamber music, operas, songs, and piano music. Among his best known compositions are the *Carnival of the Animals, Danse macabre*, and the opera *Samson and Delilah*.

My Heart at Thy Sweet Voice

(from "Samson and Delilah")

Camille Saint-Saëns

arr. by James Bastien

Slowly and expressively

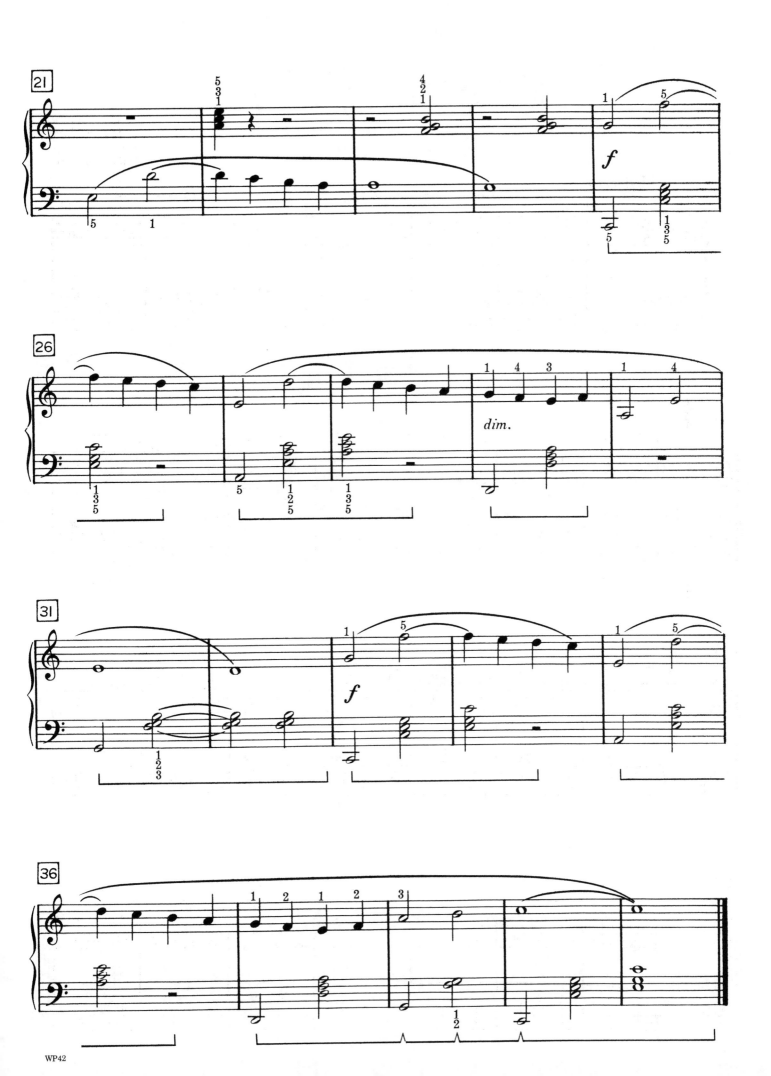

130 **Johannes Brahms (1833-1897),** German composer, first had lessons with his father who was a double-bass player at the Hamburg Opera. He began earning a living as a pianist playing in taverns and later was hired as a conductor of various orchestras. He was a friend of Clara and Robert Schumann and Franz Liszt. He wrote a great quantity of music which includes symphonies and other orchestral works, concertos, chamber music, choral music, songs, and many piano works.

Symphony No. 1

(Theme from Finale)

Johannes Brahms

arr. by James Bastien

Hungarian Dance No. 5

Johannes Brahms

arr. by James Bastien

Allegro moderato

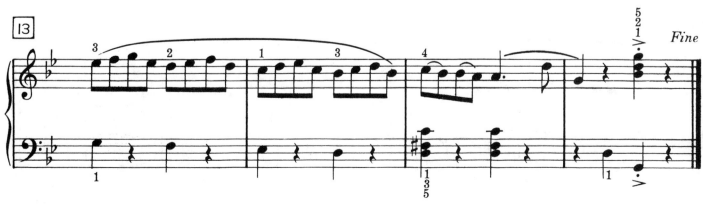

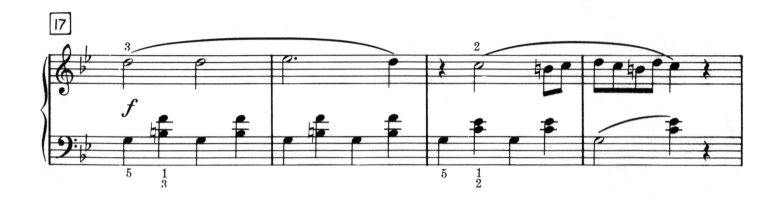

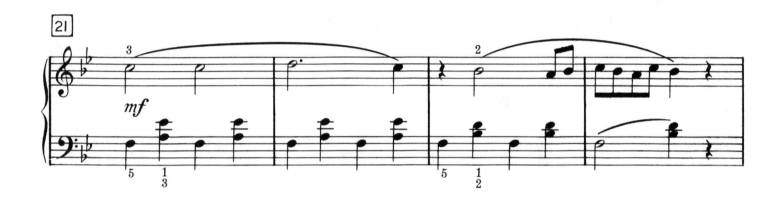

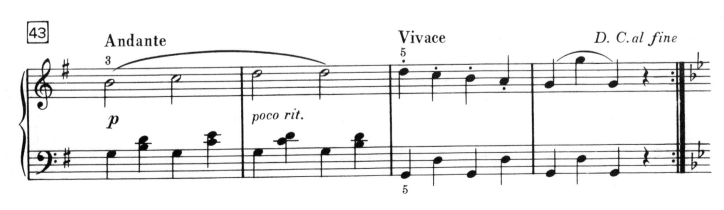

134   **Charles Gounod (1818-1893),** French composer, became best known for his opera *Faust* (1859) based on an old
German legend about a man who sells his soul to the devil in return for his youth. This secular plot is in direct
opposition to Gounod's life. He studied theology for two years, and although he decided against taking holy orders, he
was often referred to as l'Abbe Gounod. He wrote a quantity of religious works, one of his most popular being the
lovely *Ave Maria* (1859) which he adapted to the first prelude of Bach's *Well-Tempered Clavichord*.

Ave Maria

Charles Gounod

arr. by James Bastien

136 **Alexander Borodin (1833-1887),** Russian composer, was given a musical background in flute, cello, and piano. Because music was given low status in Russia at that time, many famous composers pursued other occupations. Borodin was by vocation a professor of organic chemistry. He wrote music for various mediums, and because composition was for him a slow process, some of his works were unfinished at his death. He is best remembered for his opera *Prince Igor* (completed by his friend Rimsky-Korsakov), especially the exotic, captivating *Polovetzian Dances* from this opera.

Polovetzian Dance

(from "Prince Igor")

Alexander Borodin

arr. by James Bastien

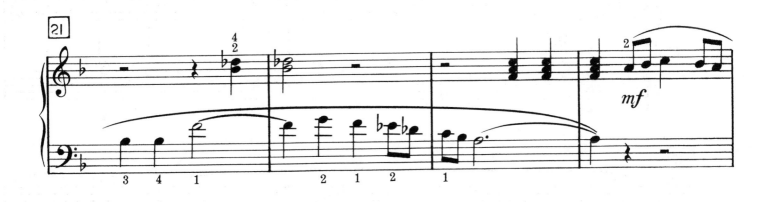

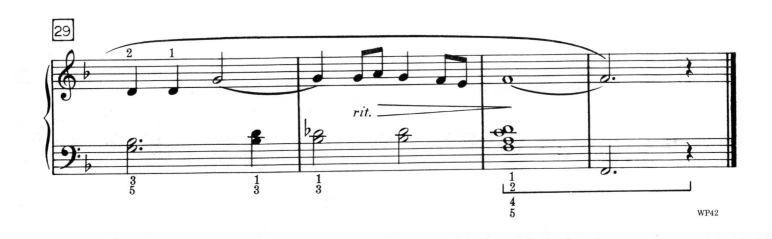

138   **Johann Strauss (1825-1899)**, Austrian composer, came from a musical family. His father, Johann, Sr., was the proprietor of a beer-house and dance-hall and a conductor and composer of light music. Johann, Jr. was not intended for a music career, and his father apprenticed him to a bookbinder. But Johann ran away and was then allowed to study the violin and composition. By the time he was nineteen he formed his own ensemble and performed as conductor of that group at a restaurant. This group received instantaneous success, and new waltzes were written for their performances. He made a tour through Austria, Germany, Poland, and Russia, and in 1872 he came to America to direct monster concerts in Boston and New York. Strauss wrote almost five hundred dance music pieces (waltzes, polkas, marches, gallops, etc.). He also wrote such operetta favorites as *Die Fledermaus (The Bat,* 1874) and *The Gypsy Baron* (1855), which are filled with famous melodies. Because of his numerous famous waltzes, he justly earned the title "Waltz King."

Emperor Waltz

Johann Strauss

arr. by James Bastien

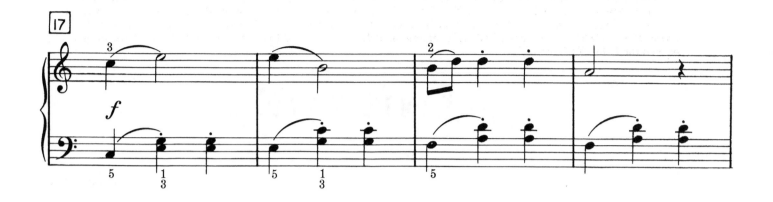

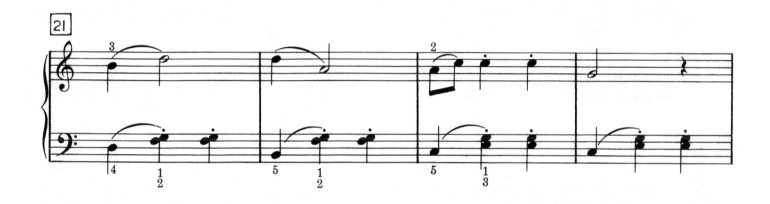

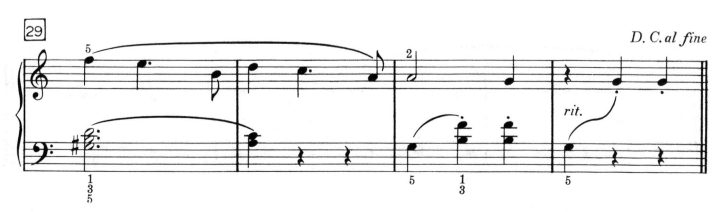

Nikolai Rimsky-Korsakov (1844-1908), Russian composer, came from an aristocratic family. He studied piano as a youngster but was trained for a navy service career. Although engaged in the navy, he began teaching composition at the St. Petersburg Conservatory when he was twenty-six, and he resigned from the navy when he was twenty-eight to pursue a musical career. He was a master of orchestration and frequently assisted in correcting friends' haphazard works. He wrote a book on the *Principles of Orchestration.* He wrote for various mediums (symphony, opera, piano, violin, etc.), but he is best remembered for *The Flight of the Bumblebee* (from the suite from the opera *Tsar Saltan*) and for his exotic programmatic symphonic suite *Scheherezade* based on the *Thousand and One Nights* which tells of Sultan Schahriar, who lost faith in women and vowed to execute every wife after spending one night with her. However, his wife, Sultana Scheherezade, beguiled her husband with 1,001 fanciful stories which impressed her husband so much that he recalled his vow.

Scheherezade

(Theme from 3rd Movement)

Nikolai Rimsky-Korsakov

arr. by James Bastien

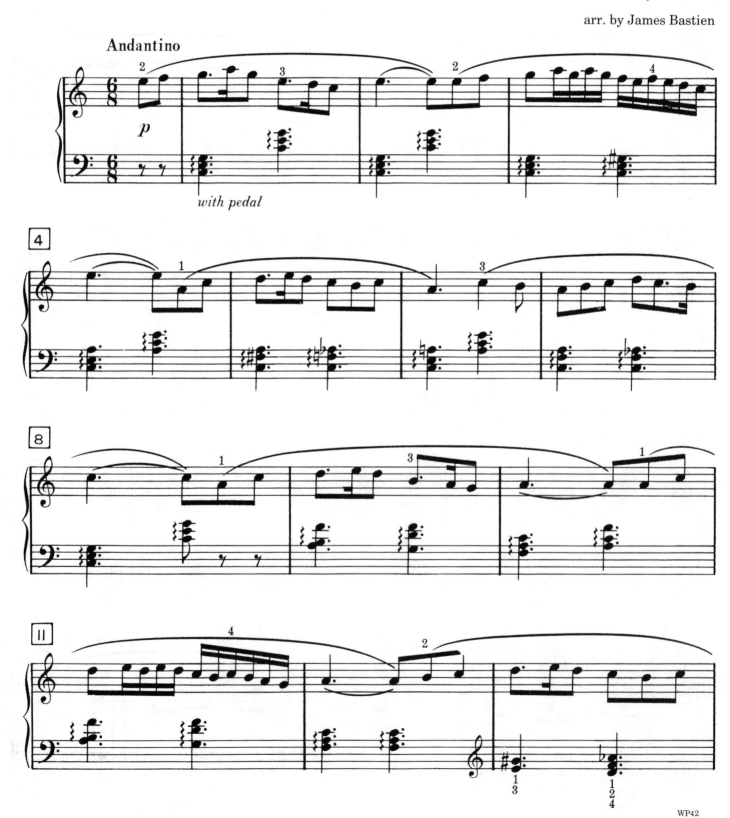

Symphony No. 5

(Theme from 2nd Movement)

Peter Ilyich Tchaikovsky

arr. by James Bastien

Andante cantabile

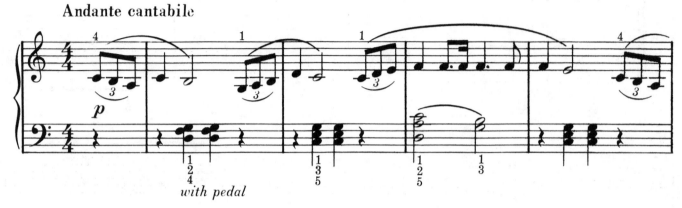

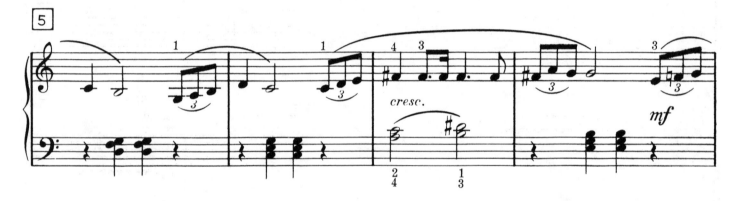

Unfinished Symphony

(Theme from 1st Movement)

Franz Schubert

arr. by James Bastien

Liebestraum

Franz Liszt

arr. by James Bastien

Moderato

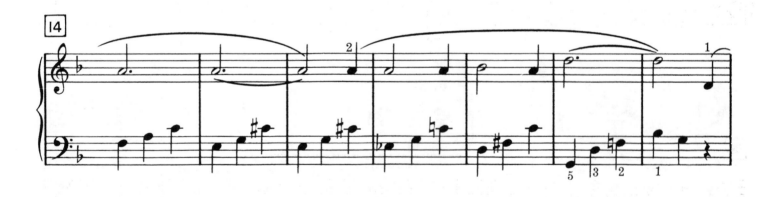

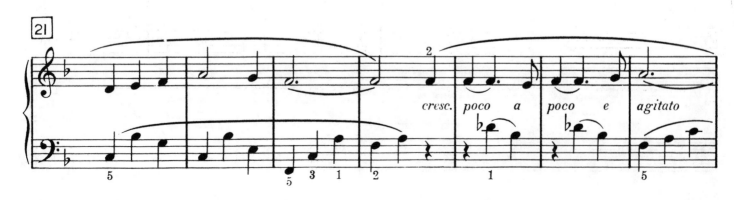

WP42

George Bizet (1838-1875), French composer, came from a musical family. His father was a singing teacher and composer; his mother was an excellent pianist. Bizet entered the Paris Conservatory at the age of nine and studied piano, organ and composition. He wrote his *First Symphony* at age seventeen. Other works include *Jeux d'enfants* (suite for piano, four-hands), *L'Arlesianne* (symphonic suite), and operas, the most famous being *Carmen*.

Toreador Song

(from "Carmen")

George Bizet

arr. by James Bastien

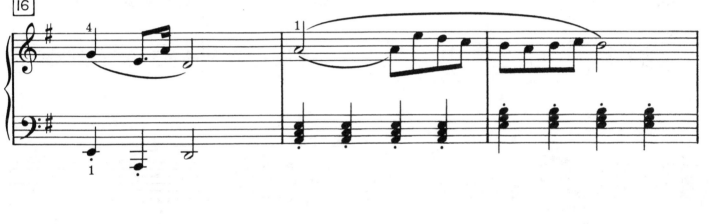

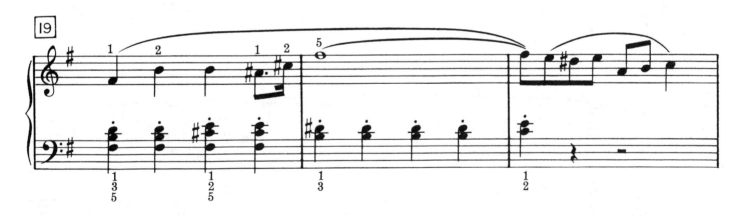

148 **Frédéric Chopin (1810-1849),** Polish composer and pianist, had a French father and a Polish mother. He showed remarkable talent as a child, and at the age of seven he played a piano concerto and performed improvisations in a public concert. In 1831 he played a piano concert in Paris and settled for most of his life there, never returning to Poland. He taught piano in Paris and performed frequently in Parisian salons. He was uneasy about playing in public and preferred composing. His works were praised by Schumann and performed by Liszt. In 1837 Liszt introduced Chopin to the author, George Sand (Madame Dudevant). Always sickly, Chopin was nursed and looked after off and on for the remainder of his life by George Sand. His illness developed into consumption which persisted to wear him down little by little. It finally killed him. Chopin wrote almost exclusively for the piano: concertos, polonaises, waltzes, etudes, mazurkas (Polish folk dances), ballades, scherzos, preludes, nocturnes, and other works. The following *Nocturne* is one of Chopin's best known pieces.

Nocturne

(Op. 9, No. 2)

Frédéric Chopin

arr. by James Bastien

Piano Concerto No. 1

(Theme from 1st Movement)

Peter Ilyich Tchaikovsky
arr. by James Bastien

Moderato e maestoso

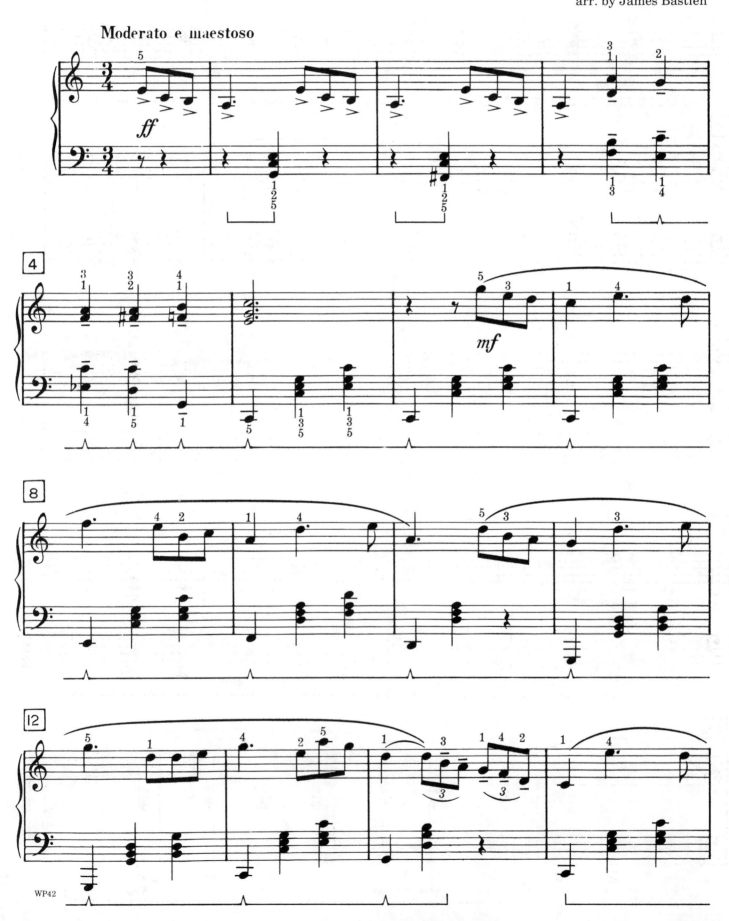

151

WP42

Fantasie Impromptu

(Op. 66)

Frédéric Chopin

arr. by James Bastien

Sergei Rachmaninoff (1873-1943), Russian pianist and composer, entered the St. Petersburg Conservatory at the age of nine to study piano and moved to Moscow when he was twelve years old to study piano with Siloti and composition with Taneyev and Arensky at the Moscow Conservatory. At the age of nineteen he wrote his celebrated *Prelude in C Sharp Minor*. Rachmaninoff was a brilliant piano virtuoso and traveled widely as a pianist and conductor. His melodic gift coupled with his immense keyboard skill produced some of the world's most hauntingly beautiful, dramatic classical music: *Second Piano Concerto, Third Piano Concerto, Rhapsody on a Theme by Paganini, Suite for Two Pianos* (Opus 17), orchestral music, songs, and other piano pieces.

Piano Concerto No. 2

(Theme from 3rd Movement)

Sergei Rachmaninoff

arr. by James Bastien

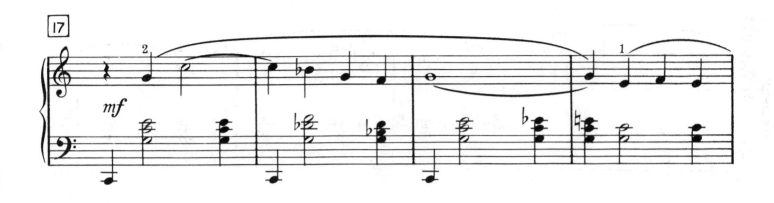

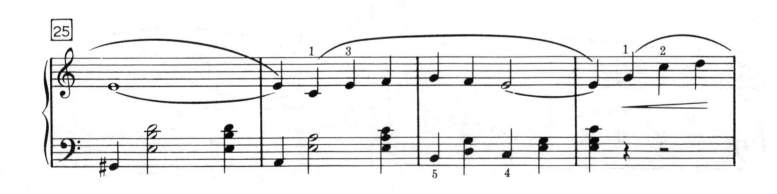

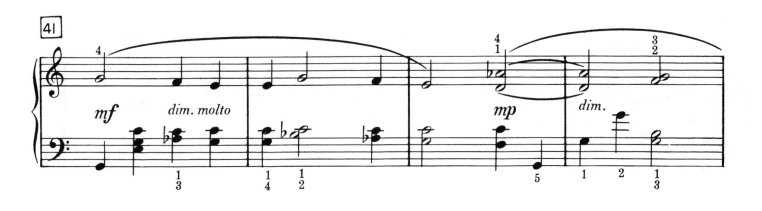

Edvard Grieg (1843-1907), Norwegian composer, received his first instruction from his mother. When he was fifteen he studied piano and theory at the Leipzig Conservatory. He returned to Norway and opened the Norwegian Academy of Music which highlighted concerts of Norwegian music. He was the conductor of the Oslo Philharmonic for many years. When he was twenty-five he performed the world premiere of his famous piano concerto playing the solo part; this composition helped to establish his prominence as a major composer of his time. Much of his music incorporates folk songs and has pronounced nationalism. Although Grieg wrote extensive compositions such as the piano concerto, piano sonata, symphonic suites (*Peer Gynt* being the best known), violin sonatas, a cello sonata, and a string quartet, he was essentially a composer in miniature forms—songs, and short piano pieces which best suited the lyric qualities of his talent.

I Love Thee

(Ich Liebe Dich)

Edvard Grieg

arr. by James Bastien

Piano Concerto in A Minor

(Theme from 1st Movement)

Edvard Grieg

arr. by James Bastien

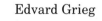

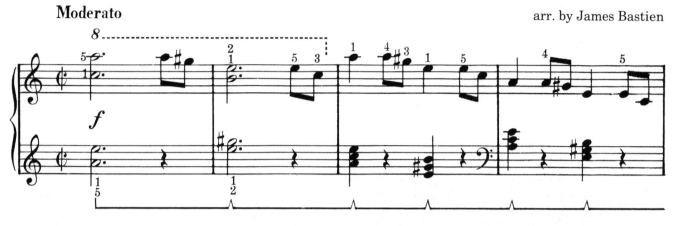

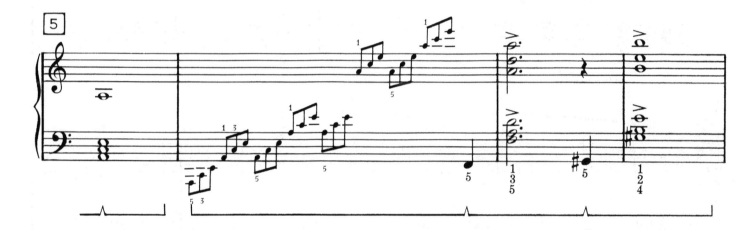